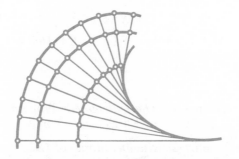

CURVES AND THEIR PROPERTIES

CLASSICS

IN MATHEMATICS EDUCATION

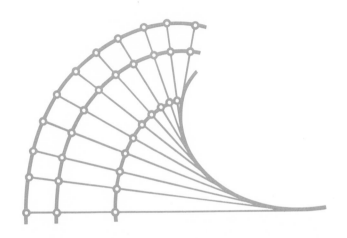

CURVES AND THEIR PROPERTIES

Robert C. Yates

THE NATIONAL COUNCIL OF TEACHERS OF MATHEMATICS

Library of Congress Catalog Card Number: 74-10222
Printed in the United States of America
1974

FOREWORD

Some mathematical works of considerable vintage have a timeless quality about them. Like classics in any field, they still bring joy and guidance to the reader. Books of this kind, if no longer readily available, are being sought out by the National Council of Teachers of Mathematics, which has begun to publish a series of such classics. The present title is the fourth volume of the series.

A Handbook on Curves and Their Properties was first published in 1952 when the author was teaching at the United States Military Academy at West Point. A photo-lithoprint reproduction was issued in 1959 by Edwards Brothers, Inc., Lithoprinters, of Ann Arbor, Michigan. The present reprint edition has been similarly produced, by photo-offset, from a copy of the 1959 edition. Except for providing new front matter, including a biographical sketch of the author and this Foreword by way of explanation, no attempt has been made to modernize the book in any way. To do so would surely detract from, rather than add to, its value.

ABOUT THE AUTHOR

Robert Carl Yates was born in Falls Church, Virginia, on 10 March 1904. In 1924 he received a B.S. degree in civil engineering from Virginia Military Institute. This degree was followed by an A.B. degree in psychology and education from Washington and Lee University in 1926 and by the M.A. and Ph.D. degrees in mathematics and applied mathematics from Johns Hopkins University in 1928 and 1930.

While working on these later degrees Bob Yates was an instructor at Virginia Military Institute, the University of Maryland, and Johns Hopkins University. After completing his Ph.D. degree, he accepted a position as assistant professor, in 1931, at the University of Maryland, where later he was promoted to associate professor. In 1939 he became associate professor of mathematics at Louisiana State University.

As a captain in the Army Reserves, Professor Yates reported to the United States Military Academy for active duty on 6 June 1942. Before leaving the Academy he rose to the rank of colonel and the title of associate professor of mathematics.

He left West Point in August 1954, when a reduction in the number of colonels was authorized at USMA, and accepted a position as professor of mathematics at Virginia Polytechnic Institute. In 1955 he became professor of mathematics and chairman of the department at the College of William and Mary. The last position he held was as one of the original professors at the University of South Florida, beginning in 1960. He went to this new institution as chairman of the Department of Mathematics, resigning the chairmanship in 1962 in order to devote more time to teaching, lecturing, and writing.

During his tour of duty at West Point, Dr. Yates spent many of his summers as a visiting professor. Among the institutions he served were Teachers College, Columbia University; Yeshiva University; and Johns Hopkins University.

Robert Yates was a man of many talents. Although he was trained in pure and applied mathematics, he became interested in the field of mathematics education rather early in his professional career. In both areas he built up a fine reputation as a lecturer and a writer. During his lifetime he had sixty-odd papers published in various research and mathematical-education journals, including the *Mathematics Teacher,* and in NCTM yearbooks. He also wrote five books dealing with various aspects of geometry, the calculus, and differential equations. From 1937 until he was called to active duty at West Point in 1942, he served on the editorial board, and as editor of one department, of the *National Mathematics Magazine.*

These were some of his professional achievements. His activities, however, were not limited to the world of mathematics. At VMI, where he was a member of the track squad, dramatics and journalism claimed some of his time. Music became a continuing resource. In later life his recreations included playing the piano as well as sailing, skating, and golf.

Dr. Yates, whose social fraternity was Kappa Alpha, was elected to two scientific honor societies: Gamma Alpha and Sigma Xi. Holding membership in the American Mathematical Society, the Mathematical Association of America, and the National Council of Teachers of Mathematics, he was at one period a governor of the MAA. He was also a member of the MAA's original ad hoc Committee on the Undergraduate Program in Mathematics (CUPM). In late 1961 he was selected by the Association of Higher Education as one of twenty-five "outstanding college and university educators in America today," and on 4 February 1962 he was featured on the ABC-TV program "Meet the Professor."

Dr. Yates had been interested in mathematics education before 1939. However, when he came to Louisiana State University, his work in this field began to expand. Owing to his efforts, the Department of Mathematics and the College of Education made some important changes in the mathematical curriculum for the training of prospective secondary school teachers. One of the most important additions was six semester hours in geometry. Dr. Yates was given this course to teach, and for a text he used his first book, *Geometrical Tools.* From this beginning his interest and work in mathematics education increased, while he continued to lecture and write in the areas of pure and applied mathematics.

The atmosphere at West Point was quite a change for Dr. Yates. However, even here he continued his activities in mathematics education. One of his duties was to supervise and conduct courses in the techniques of teaching mathematics. These were courses designed for the groups of new instructors who joined the department staff annually; for most of the faculty at the Academy, then as now, were active-duty officers who came on a first or second tour of three to four years' duration. In performing this duty he was considered a superior instructor and also an excellent teacher of teachers.

After leaving the service Professor Yates continued his efforts to improve mathematics education. During the summers he taught in several different mathematics institutes, and he was a guest lecturer in many summer and academic-year institutes supported by the National Science Foundation. In earlier years he both taught and lectured in the grandfather of all institutes, the one developed by Professor W. W. Rankin at Duke University. In Virginia and later in Florida he served as a consultant to teachers of mathematics in various school districts. During the academic years 1961/62 and 1962/63 the University of South Florida was engaged in an experimental television program. Professor Yates was the television lecturer in the course materials developed through this program. As a result of this program as well as the MAA lectureship program for high schools, supported by the NSF, he traveled to all parts of Florida giving lectures and consulting with high school teachers.

Through all these activities Dr. Yates greatly enhanced the field of mathematics education. He built up a reputation as an outstanding lecturer with a pleasing, interest-provoking presentation and a rare ability to talk while illustrating his subject. Those who have heard him will long remember him and his great ability. Others will find that his writings show, somewhat vicariously, these same characteristics.

By his first wife, Naomi Sherman, who died in childbirth, he had three children. Robert Jefferson, the eldest, is now in business in California. Melinda Susan, the youngest, is now Mrs. Richard B. Shaw, the wife of a Missouri surgeon. Mrs. Shaw majored in mathematics at Mount Holyoke College and works as a computer programmer and systems analyst. The second child is Daniel Sherman. He is following in his father's footsteps and has completed his doctorate in mathematics education at Florida State University. He is a mathematics specialist at the Mathematics and Science Center, a resource center serving the public schools in the city of Richmond, Virginia, and in the counties of Chesterfield, Goochland, Henrico, and Powhatan.

Dr. Yates passed away on 18 December 1963 and was interred in Arlington National Cemetery.

HOUSTON T. KARNES

Louisiana State University

NOTATION

x, y = Rectangular Coordinates.

ρ, r = Polar Coordinate, (Radius Vector).

θ = Parameter or Polar Coordinate.

φ = Inclination of Tangent.

ψ = Angle between a Tangent and the Radius Vector to Point of Tangency.

s = Arc Length.

σ = Arc of Evolute (or Standard Deviation).

p = Distance from Origin to Tangent.

L = Length; A = Area; V = Volume; Σ = Surface Area.

Σ_x = Surface of Revolution about the X-axis.

V_x = Volume of Revolution about the X-axis.

N = Normal Length.

R = Radius of Curvature.

K = Curvature.

v = Velocity; a = Acceleration.

$' = \dfrac{d}{dx}$; $\cdot = \dfrac{d}{dt}$ (t = Time or a Parameter).

$F_x = \dfrac{dF}{dx}$, (or $\dfrac{\partial F}{\partial x}$).

$i = \sqrt{-1}$.

$z = x + iy$, a Complex Variable.

$f(s, \varphi) = 0$: The Whewell Intrinsic Equation.

$f(R, s) = 0$: The Cesáro Intrinsic Equation.

$f(r, p) = 0$: The Pedal Equation.

CONTENTS

CONTENTS

PREFACE

This volume proposes to supply to student and teacher a quick reference on properties of plane curves. Rather than a systematic or comprehensive study of curve theory, it is a collection of information which might be found useful in the classroom and in engineering practice. The alphabetical arrangement is given to aid in the search for this information.

It seemed necessary to incorporate sections on such topics as Evolutes, Curve Sketching, and Intrinsic Equations to make the items and properties listed under various curves readily understandable. If the book is used as a text, it would be desirable to present the material in the following order:

I	II
ANALYSIS and SYSTEMS	CURVES
Caustics	Astroid
Curvature	Cardioid
Envelopes	Cassinian Curves
Evolutes	Catenary
Functions with Discontinuous	Circle
Properties	Cissoid
Glissettes	Conchoid
Instantaneous Centers	Conics
Intrinsic Equations	Cubic Parabola
Inversion	Cycloid
Involutes	Deltoid
Isoptic Curves	Epi- and Hypocycloid
Parallel Curves	Exponential Curves
Pedal Curves	Folium of Descartes
Pedal Equations	Hyperbolic Functions
Radial Curves	Kieroid
Roulettes	Lemniscate
Sketching	Limacon
Trochoids	Nephroid
	Pursuit Curves
	Semi-cubic Parabola
	Spirals
	Strophoid
	Tractrix
	Trigonometric Functions
	Witch

PREFACE

Since derivations of all properties would make the volume cumbersome and somewhat devoid of general interest, explanations are frequently omitted. It is thought possible for the reader to supply many of them without difficulty.

Space is provided occasionally for the reader to insert notes, proofs, and references of his own and thus fit the material to his particular interests.

It is with pleasure that the author acknowledges valuable assistance in the composition of this work. Mr. H. T. Guard criticized the manuscript and offered helpful suggestions; Mr. Charles Roth and Mr. William Bobalke assisted in the preparation of the drawings; Mr. Thomas Vecchio lent expert clerical aid. Appreciation is also due Colonel Harris Jones who encouraged the project.

Robert C. Yates
West Point, N. Y.
June 1947

For an informative account see "Historical Stages in the Definition of Curves" by C. B. Boyer in National Mathematics Magazine, XIX (1944-5) 294-310.

ASTROID

HISTORY: The Cycloidal curves, including the Astroid, were discovered by Roemer (1674) in his search for the best form for gear teeth. Double generation was first noticed by Daniel Bernoulli in 1725.

1. DESCRIPTION: The Astroid is a hypocycloid of four cusps: The locus of a point P on a circle rolling upon the inside of another with radius four times as large.

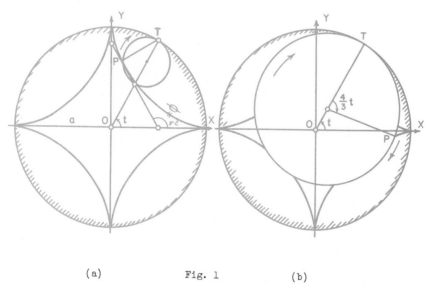

(a)   Fig. 1   (b)

Double Generation: It may also be described by a point on a circle of radius $\frac{3a}{4}$ rolling upon the inside of a fixed circle of radius a. (See Epicycloids)

2. EQUATIONS:

$$x^{\frac{2}{3}} + y^{\frac{2}{3}} = a^{\frac{2}{3}} \quad \begin{cases} x = a\cos^3 t = (\frac{a}{4})(3\cos t + \cos 3t) \\ y = a\sin^3 t = (\frac{a}{4})(3\sin t - \sin 3t) \end{cases}$$

$$r^2 = a^2 - 3p^2$$
$$R^2 + 4s^2 = \frac{9a^2}{4}$$

$$s = (\frac{3a}{4})\cdot\cos 2\varphi$$

3. METRICAL PROPERTIES:

$$L = 6a \qquad\qquad\qquad A = (\frac{3}{8})(\pi a^2)$$

$$V_x = (\frac{32}{105})(\pi a^3) \qquad \Sigma_x = (\frac{12}{5})(\pi a^2)$$

$$\varphi = \pi - t \qquad\qquad R = (\frac{3a}{2})\cdot\sin 2t = 3\sqrt[3]{axy}$$

4. GENERAL ITEMS:

(a) Its <u>evolute</u> is another Astroid. [See Evolutes 4(b).]

(b) It is the <u>envelope</u> of a family of Ellipses, the sum of whose axes is constant. (Fig. 2b)

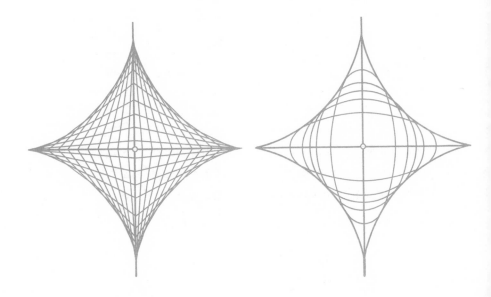

(a)   Fig. 2   (b)

(c) The <u>length</u> <u>of</u> <u>its</u> <u>tangent</u> intercepted between the cusp tangents is constant. Thus it is the <u>envelope</u> of a Trammel of Archimedes. (Fig. 2a)

(d) Its <u>orthoptic</u> with respect to its center is the curve

$$r^2 = (\frac{a^2}{2}) \cdot \cos^2 2\theta.$$

(e) <u>Tangent</u> <u>Construction</u>: (Fig. 1) Through P draw the circle with center on the circle of radius $\frac{3a}{4}$ which is tangent to the fixed circle as at T (left-hand figure). Since the instantaneous center of rotation of P is T, TP is normal to the curve at P.

BIBLIOGRAPHY

Edwards, J.: <u>Calculus</u>, Macmillan (1892) 337.
Salmon, G.: <u>Higher</u> <u>Plane</u> <u>Curves</u>, Dublin (1879) 278.
Wieleitner, H.: <u>Spezielle</u> <u>ebene</u> <u>Kurven</u>, Leipzig (1908).
Williamson, B.: <u>Differential</u> <u>Calculus</u>, Longmans, Green (1895) 339.
Section on <u>Epicycloids</u>, herein.

CARDIOID

HISTORY: The Cardioid is a member of the family of Cycloidal Curves, first studied by Roemer (1674) in an investigation for the best form of gear teeth.

1. DESCRIPTION: The Cardioid is an Epicycloid of one
cusp: the locus of a point P of a circle rolling upon
the outside of another of equal size. (Fig. 3a)

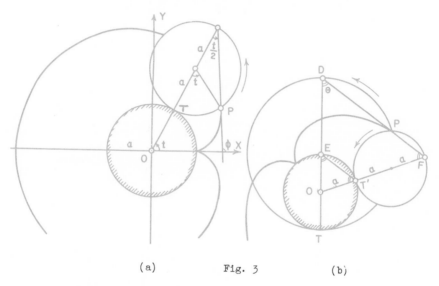

(a)   Fig. 3   (b)

Double Generation: (Fig. 3b). Let the curve be generated by the point P on the rolling circle of radius a.
Draw ET', OT'F, and PT' to T. Draw FP to D and the circle
through T, P, D. Since angle DPT = $\frac{\pi}{2}$, this last circle
has DT as diameter. Now, PD is parallel to T'E and from
similar triangles, DE = 2a. Moreover, arc TT' = $a\theta$ =
arc T'P = arc T'X. Accordingly,

$$\text{arc TT'X} = 2a\theta = \text{arc TP}.$$

Thus the curve may be described as an Epicycloid in two
ways: by a circle of radius a, or by one of radius 2a,
rolling as shown upon a fixed circle of radius a.

2. EQUATIONS:

$$(x^2 + y^2 \mp 2ax)^2 = 4a^2(x^2 + y^2) \text{(Origin at cusp)}.$$

$$r = 2a(1 \pm \cos\theta), \ r = 2a(1 \pm \sin\theta)\text{(Origin at cusp)}.$$

$$9(r^2 - a^2) = 8p^2. \text{ (Origin at center of fixed circle)}.$$

$$\begin{cases} x = a(2\cos t - \cos 2t) \\ y = a(2\sin t - \sin 2t) \end{cases}, \quad z = a(2e^{it} - e^{2it}).$$

$$r^3 = 4ap^2. \qquad\qquad s = 8a\cdot\cos\left(\frac{\varphi}{3}\right).$$

$$9R^2 + s^2 = 64a^2.$$

3. METRICAL PROPERTIES:

$$L = 16a. \qquad\qquad A = 6\pi a^2$$

$$\varphi = \left(\frac{3}{2}\right)t \qquad\qquad \Sigma_x = \left(\frac{128}{5}\right)(\pi a^2)$$

$$R = \frac{2}{3}\sqrt{2ar} \text{ for } r = a(1 - \cos\theta).$$

4. GENERAL ITEMS:

(a) It is the inverse of a parabola with respect to
its focus.

(b) Its evolute is another cardioid.

(c) It is the pedal of a circle with respect to a
point on the circle.

(d) It is a special limacon: $r = a + b\cos\theta$ with
$a = b$.

(e) It is the caustic of a circle with radiant point
on the circle.

(f) The tangents at the three points whose subtended angles, measured at the cusp, differ by
$\frac{2\pi}{3}$ are parallel.

(g) The sum of the distances from the cusp to the four
intersections with an arbitrary line is constant.

(h) <u>Cam</u>. If the cardioid be pivoted at the cusp and rotated with constant angular velocity, a pin, constrained to a fixed straight line and bearing on the Cardioid, will move with simple harmonic motion. Thus for

$$r = a(1 + \cos \theta),$$
$$\dot{r} = -(a \sin \theta)\dot{\theta},$$
$$\ddot{r} = -(a \cos \theta)\dot{\theta}^2 - (a \sin \theta)\ddot{\theta}.$$

If $\dot{\theta} = k$, a constant:

$$\ddot{r} = -k^2(a \cos \theta) = -k^2(r - a),$$

or

$$\frac{d^2}{dt^2}(r - a) = -k^2(r - a),$$

the differential equation characterizing the motion of any point of the pin.

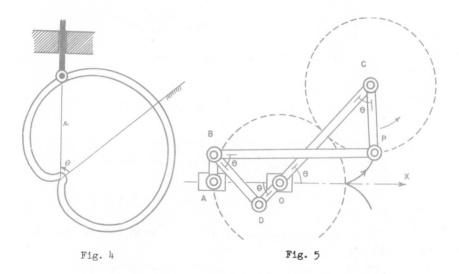

Fig. 4   **Fig. 5**

(i) The curve is the locus of the point P of two similar (Proportional) crossed parallelograms, joined as shown, with points O and A fixed.

AB = OD = b; AO = BD = CP = a; BP = DC = c = b + 2a.

and $a^2 = bc.$

At all times, angle PCO = θ = angle COX. Any point rigidly attached to CP describes a Limacon.

BIBLIOGRAPHY

Keown and Faires: Mechanism, McGraw Hill (1931).
Morley and Morley: Inversive Geometry, Ginn (1933) 239.
Yates, R.C.: Geometrical Tools, Educational Publishers,
    St. Louis (1949) 182.

CASSINIAN CURVES

HISTORY: Studied by Giovanni Domenico Cassini in 1680 in connection with the relative motions of earth and sun.

1. DESCRIPTION: A Cassinian Curve is the locus of a point P the product of whose distances from two fixed points F_1, F_2 is constant (here = k^2).

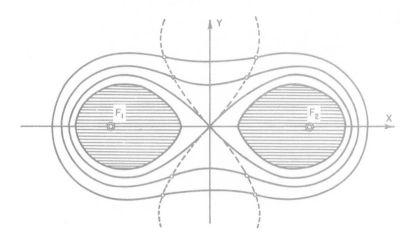

Fig. 6

2. EQUATIONS:

$$[(x - a)^2 + y^2] \cdot [(x + a)^2 + y^2] = k^4.$$

$$r^4 + a^4 - 2r^2a^2 \cos 2\theta = k^4.$$

$$[F_1 = (-a,o) \quad F_2 = (a,o)]$$

3. METRICAL PROPERTIES:

(See Section on Lemniscate)

4. GENERAL ITEMS:

(a) Let <u>b</u> - <u>a</u> be the inner radius of a <u>torus</u> whose generating circle has radius <u>a</u>. The section formed by a plane parallel to the axis of the torus and distant <u>a</u> units from it is a Cassinian. If b = 2a this plane is an inner tangent to the surface and the section is a <u>Lemniscate</u>.

(b) The set of Cassinian Curves

$$(x^2 + y^2)^2 + A(y^2 - x^2)$$

$$+ B = 0, \ B \neq 0,$$

inverts into itself.

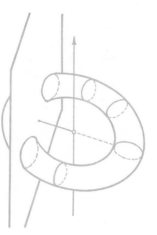

(c) If k = a, the Cassinian is the <u>Lemniscate of Bernoulli</u>: $r^2 = 2a^2 \cos 2\theta$, a curve that is the <u>inverse</u> and <u>pedal</u>, with respect to its center, of a Rectangular Hyperbola.

Fig. 7

(d) The points P and P' of the linkage shown in Fig. 8 describe the curve. Here AD = AO = OB = a; DC = CQ = EO = OC = $\frac{c}{2}$; CP = PE = EP' = P'C = d.

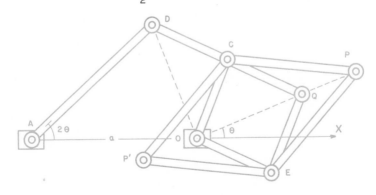

Fig. 8

Let the coordinates of Q and P be (ρ, θ) and (r, θ), respectively. Since O, D, and Q lie on a circle with center at C, the lines DO and OQ are always at right angles. Thus

$$(OQ)^2 = (DQ)^2 - (DO)^2 \quad \text{or} \quad \rho^2 = c^2 - 4a^2 \sin^2\theta.$$

The attached Peaucellier cell inverts the point Q to P under the property

$$r(r - \rho) = d^2 - \frac{c^2}{4}.$$

Thus, eliminating ρ between the last two relations:

$$(d^2 - \frac{c^2}{4} - r^2)^2 = r^2 c^2 - 4r^2 a^2 \sin^2\theta.$$

or, in rectangular coordinates:

$$(x^2 + y^2)^2 + Ax^2 + By^2 + C = 0,$$

a curve that may be identified as a Cassinian if

$$d = \sqrt{a^2 - \frac{c^2}{4}}.$$

(e) The locus of the flex points of a family of con-focal Cassinian curves is a <u>Lemniscate</u> of Bernoulli (Fig. 6).

5. POINTWISE CONSTRUCTION:

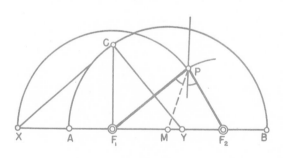

Fig. 9

Let the foci, Fig. 9, be F_1, F_2; the constant product k^2. Lay off $F_1C = k$ perpendicular to F_1F_2. Draw the circle with center F_1 and any radius F_1X. Draw CX and its perpendicular CY. Then

$$(F_1X) \cdot (F_1Y) = k^2$$

and thus F_1X and F_1Y are focal radii (measured from F_1 and F_2) of a point P on the curve. (From symmetry, four points are constructible from these two radii.) M is the midpoint of F_1F_2 and A and B are extreme points of the curves.

BIBLIOGRAPHY

Salmon, G.: Higher Plane Curves, Dublin (1879) 44,126.
Willson, F. N.: Graphics, Graphics Press (1909) 74.
Williamson, B.: Calculus, Longmans, Green (1895) 233,333.
Yates, R.C.: Geometrical Tools, Educational Publishers,
    St. Louis (1949) 186.

CATENARY

HISTORY: Galileo was the first to investigate the Catenary which he mistook for a Parabola. James Bernoulli
in 1691 obtained its true form and gave some of its
properties.

1. DESCRIPTION: The Catenary is the form assumed by a
perfectly flexible inextensible chain of uniform density
hanging from two supports not in the same vertical line.

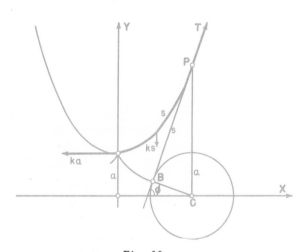

Fig. 10

2. EQUATIONS: If T is the tension at any point P,

$$\left.\begin{array}{l} T \cos \varphi = ka \\ T \sin \varphi = ks \end{array}\right\} \quad s = ay' = a \tan \varphi \ ; \ aR = a^2 + s^2$$

$$y = a \cdot \cosh\left(\frac{x}{a}\right) = \left(\frac{a}{2}\right)\left(e^{\frac{x}{a}} + e^{-\frac{x}{a}}\right) \quad ; \quad y^2 = a^2 + s^2 .$$

3. METRICAL PROPERTIES:

$A = a \cdot s = 2(\text{area triangle PCB})$ $\Sigma_x = \pi(ys + ax)$

$R = \dfrac{y^2}{a}$ $V_x = (\dfrac{a}{2}) \cdot \Sigma_x$

$N = -R.$

4. GENERAL ITEMS:

(a) The tangent at any point (x,y) is also tangent to a circle of radius $\underline{a}$, with center at $(x,0)$.

$[y' = \sinh(\dfrac{x}{a}) = \pm \dfrac{\sqrt{y^2 - a^2}}{a}]$.

(b) Tangents drawn to the curves $y = e^{\frac{x}{a}}$, $y = e^{-\frac{x}{a}}$, $y = a \cosh \dfrac{x}{a}$ at points having the same abscissa are concurrent.

(c) The path of B, an involute of the catenary, is the Tractrix. (Since $\tan \theta = \dfrac{s}{a}$, PB = s).

(d) As a roulette, it is the locus of the focus of a parabola rolling along a line. (See Envelopes, 5g).

(e) It is a plane section of the surface of least area (a soap film catenoid) spanning two circular disks, Fig. 11a. (This is the only minimal surface of revolution.)

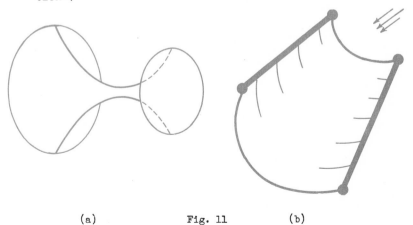

(a)   Fig. 11   (b)

(f) It is a <u>plane</u> <u>section</u> <u>of</u> <u>a</u> <u>sail</u> bounded by two
rods with the wind perpendicular to the plane of the
rods, such that the pressure on any element of the
sail is normal to the element and proportional to the
square of the velocity, Fig. 11b. (See Routh)

BIBLIOGRAPHY

<u>Encyclopaedia</u> <u>Britannica</u>, 14th Ed. under "Curves,
    Special".
Routh, E. J.: <u>Analytical</u> <u>Statics</u>, 2nd Ed. (1896) I ₦ 458,
    p. 310.
Salmon, G.: <u>Higher</u> <u>Plane</u> <u>Curves</u>, Dublin (1879) 287.
Wallis: <u>Edinburgh</u> <u>Trans</u>. XIV, 625.

CAUSTICS

HISTORY: Caustics were first introduced and studied by Tschirnhausen in 1682. Other contributors were Huygens, Quetelet, Lagrange, and Cayley.

1. A <u>caustic</u> curve is the envelope of light rays, emitted from a radiant point source S, after reflection or refraction by a given curve f = 0. The caustics by reflection and refraction are called <u>catacaustic</u> and <u>diacaustic</u>, respectively.

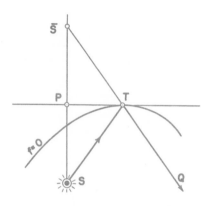

Fig. 12

2. An <u>orthotomic</u> curve (or secondary caustic) is the locus of the point $\overline{S}$, the reflection of S in the tangent at T. (See also Pedal Curves.)

3. The instantaneous center of motion of $\overline{S}$ is T. Thus <u>the caustic is the envelope of normals</u>, TQ, <u>to the orthotomic</u>; i.e., <u>the caustic is the evolute of the orthotomic</u>.

4. The locus of P is the <u>pedal</u> of the reflecting curve with respect to S. Thus the orthotomic is a curve <u>similar</u> to the pedal with <u>double</u> its linear dimensions.

5. The <u>Catacaustic</u> <u>of</u> <u>a</u> <u>circle</u> is the evolute of a limacon whose pole is the radiant point. With usual x,y axes
[radius <u>a</u>, radiant point (c,0)], the equation of the
caustic is:

$$[(4c^2 - a^2)(x^2 + y^2) - 2a^2cx - a^2c^2]^3 - 27a^4c^2y^2(x^2 + y^2 - c^2)^2 = 0.$$

For various radiant points C, these exhibit the following forms:

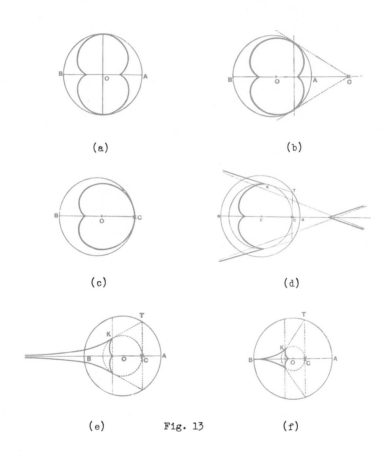

(a)   (b)

(c)   (d)

(e)   Fig. 13   (f)

6. In two particular cases, the caustics of a circle of radius _a_ may be determined in the following elementary way:

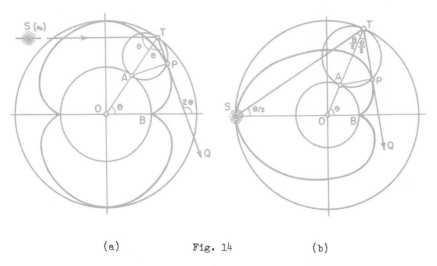

(a)   Fig. 14   (b)

With the source S at ∝, the incident and reflected rays make angles θ with the normal at T. Thus the fixed circle O(A) of radius a/2 has its arc AB equal to the arc AP of the circle through A, P, T of radius a/4. The point P of this latter circle generates the Nephroid and the reflected ray TPQ is its tangent (AP is perpendicular to TP).

With the source S on the circle, the incident and reflected rays makes angles θ/2 with the normal at T. Thus the fixed circle and the equal rolling circle have arcs AB and AP equal. The point P generates a Cardioid and TPQ is its tangent (AP is perpendicular to TP).

These are the bright curves seen on the surface of coffee in a cup or upon the table inside of a napkin ring.

7. <u>The</u> <u>Caustics</u> <u>by</u> <u>Refraction</u> (<u>Diacaustics</u>) <u>at</u> <u>a</u> <u>Line</u> <u>L</u>.
SQ is incident, QT refracted, and $\overline{S}$ is the reflection of
S in L. Produce TQ to meet the variable circle drawn
through S, Q, and $\overline{S}$ in P. Let the angles of incidence
and refraction be θ_1 and θ_2 and $\mu = \dfrac{\sin \theta_1}{\sin \theta_2}$ be the index
of refraction. Now SP and $\overline{S}$P make equal angles with the
refracted ray PQT. Thus in passing from a dense to a
rare medium ($\theta_1 < \theta_2$) and vice versa ($\theta_1 > \theta_2$):

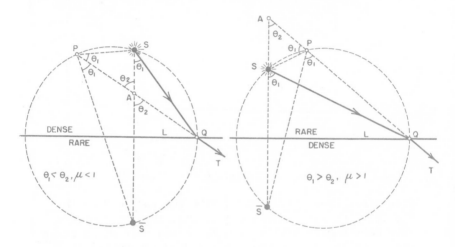

Fig. 15

$$\mu = \frac{\sin \theta_1}{\sin \theta_2} = \frac{AS}{PS} = \frac{A\overline{S}}{P\overline{S}} \ .$$

$$\mu = \frac{AS + A\overline{S}}{PS + P\overline{S}} = \frac{S\overline{S}}{PS + P\overline{S}} \cdot$$

Thus, since $S\overline{S}$ is constant,

$$PS + P\overline{S} = S\overline{S}/\mu$$

a constant. The locus of P is then an <u>ellipse</u> with S, $\overline{S}$ as foci, major axis $S\overline{S}/\mu$, eccentricity μ, and with PQT as its normal. The envelope of these rays PQT, normal to the ellipse, is its evolute, the caustic. (Fig. 16)

$$\mu = \frac{A\overline{S} - AS}{P\overline{S} - PS} = \frac{S\overline{S}}{P\overline{S} - PS} \cdot$$

Thus, since $S\overline{S}$ is constant,

$$P\overline{S} - PS = S\overline{S}/\mu$$

a constant. The locus of P is then an <u>hyperbola</u> with S, $\overline{S}$ as foci, major axis $S\overline{S}/\mu$, eccentricity μ, and with PQT as its normal. The envelope of these rays PQT, normal to the hyperbola is its evolute, the caustic. (Fig. 17)

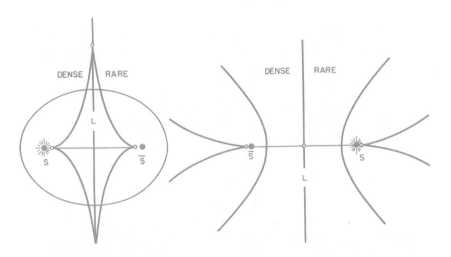

Fig. 16   Fig. 17

8. SOME EXAMPLES:

(a) If the radiant point is the focus of a parabola, the caustic of the evolute of that parabola is the evolute of another <u>parabola</u>.

(b) If the radiant point is at the vertex of a reflecting parabola, the caustic is the evolute of a cissoid.

(c) If the radiant point is the center of a circle, the caustic of the involute of that circle is the evolute of the spiral of Archimedes.

(d) If the radiant point is the center of a conic, the reflected rays are all normal to the quartic $r^2 = A \cos 2\theta + B$, having the radiant point as double point.

(e) If the radiant point moves along a fixed diameter of a reflecting circle of radius a, the two cusps of the caustic which do not lie on that diameter move on the curve $r = a \cdot \cos(\frac{\theta}{2})$.

(f) If the radiant point is the pole of the reflecting spiral $r = ae^{\theta \, \text{ctn} \, \alpha}$, the caustic is a similar spiral.

(g) If light rays parallel to the y-axis fall upon the reflecting curve $y = e^x$, the caustic is a catenary.

(h) The orthotomic of a parabola for rays perpendicular to its axis is the sinusoidal spiral
$r = a \cdot \sec^3(\frac{\theta}{3})$.

BIBLIOGRAPHY

American Mathematical Monthly: 28(1921) 182,187.
Cayley, A.: "Memoir on Caustics", Philosophical Transactions (1856).
Heath, R. S.: Geometrical Optics (1895) 105.
Salmon, G.: Higher Plane Curves, Dublin (1879) 98.

THE CIRCLE

1. DESCRIPTION: A circle is a plane continuous curve all of whose points are equidistant from a fixed coplanar point.

2. EQUATIONS:

$$(x - h)^2 + (y - k)^2 = a^2$$

$$x^2 + y^2 + Ax + By + C = 0$$

$$\begin{vmatrix} x^2 + y^2 & x & y & 1 \\ x_1^2 + y_1^2 & x_1 & y_1 & 1 \\ x_2^2 + y_2^2 & x_2 & y_2 & 1 \\ x_3^2 + y_3^2 & x_3 & y_3 & 1 \end{vmatrix} = 0$$

$$\begin{cases} x = h + a \cos \theta \\ y = k + a \sin \theta \end{cases}$$

$$s = a \varphi$$

$$R = a$$

$$pa = r^2$$

3. METRICAL PROPERTIES:

$$L = 2\pi a \qquad\qquad \Sigma = 4\pi a^2 \qquad\qquad R = a$$

$$A = \pi a^2 \qquad\qquad V = \frac{4\pi a^3}{3}$$

4. GENERAL ITEMS:

(a) The Secant Property. Fig. 18(a). If lines are drawn from a fixed point P intersecting a fixed circle, the product of the segments in which the circle divides each line is constant; i.e., PA·PB = PD·PC (since the arc subtended by $\angle$ BCD plus that subtended by $\angle$ BAD is the entire circumference, triangles PAD and PBC are similar). To evaluate this constant, p, draw the line through P and the center O of the circle. Then $(PO - a)(PO + a) = p = (PO)^2 - a^2$.

The quantity p is called the power of the point P with respect to the circle. If $p <, = , > 0$, P lies respectively inside, on, outside the circle.

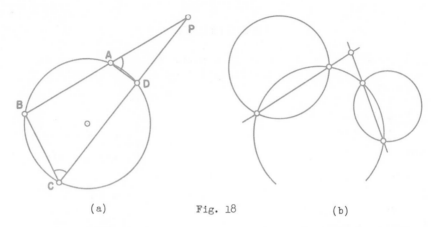

(a)   Fig. 18   (b)

The locus of all points P which have equal power with
respect to two fixed circles is a line called the
radical axis of the two circles. If the circles intersect, the radical axis is their common chord.
Fig. 18(b).

The three radical axes of three circles intersect in
a point called the radical center, a point having
equal power with respect to each of the circles and
equidistant from them.

Thus to construct the radical axis of two circles,
first draw a third arbitrary circle to intersect the
two. Common chords meet on the required axis.

(b) Similitude. Any two coplanar circles have centers
of similitude: the intersections I and E (collinear
with the centers) of lines joining extremities of
parallel diameters.

The six centers of similitude of three circles lie by
threes on four straight lines.

The excenter of similitude of the circumcircle and
nine-point circle of a triangle is its orthocenter.

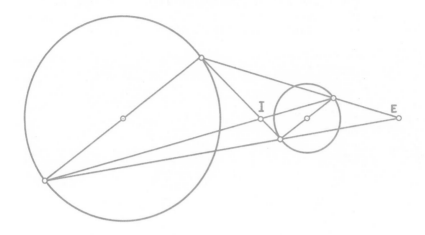

Fig. 19

(c) <u>The Problem of Apollonius</u> is that of constructing a circle tangent to three given non-coaxal circles (generally eight solutions). The problem is reducible (see Inversion) to that of drawing a circle through three specified points.

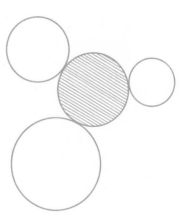

Fig. 20

(d) <u>Trains</u>. A series of circles each drawn tangent to
two given non-intersecting circles and to another member of the series is called a <u>train</u>. It is not to be

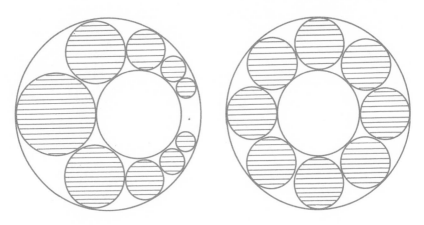

Fig. 21

expected that such a series generally will close upon
itself. If such is the case, however, the series is
called a <u>Steiner chain</u>.

<u>Any</u> Steiner chain can be inverted into a Steiner
chain tangent to two concentric circles.

Two concentric circles admit a Steiner chain of $\underline{n}$
circles, encircling the common center $\underline{k}$ times if the
angle subtended at the center by each circle of the
train is commensurable with $360°$, i.e., equal to

$$(\frac{k}{n})(360°).$$

If two circles admit a Steiner chain, they admit an
infinitude of such chains.

(e) <u>Arbelos</u>. The
figure bounded by
the semicircular
arcs AXB, BYC, AZC
(A,B,C collinear)
is the <u>arbelos</u> or
<u>shoemaker's knife</u>.
Studied by Archi-
medes, some of its
properties are:

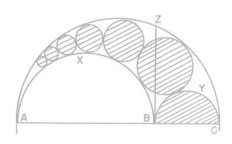

1. $\widehat{AXB} + \widehat{BYC} = \widehat{AZC}$.

2. Its area equals

Fig. 22

the area of the circle on BZ as a diameter.

3. Circles inscribed in the three-sided figures ABZ,
CBZ are equal with diameter $\dfrac{(AB)(BC)}{(AC)}$

4. (Pappus) Consider a train of circles c_0, c_1, c_2,
... all tangent to the circles on AC and AB (c_0 is
the circle BC). If r_n is the radius of c_n, and h_n the
distance from its center to ABC,

$$\boxed{h_n = 2n \cdot r_n}$$ (Invert, using A as center.)

BIBLIOGRAPHY

Daus, P. H.: <u>College Geometry</u>, Prentice-Hall (1941).
Johnson, R. A.: <u>Modern Geometry</u>, Houghton Mifflin (1929)
    113.
Mackay, J. S.: <u>Proc. Ed. Math. Soc.</u> III (1884) 2.
Shively, L. S.: <u>Modern Geometry</u>, John Wiley (1939) 151.

CISSOID

HISTORY: Diocles (between 250-100 BC) utilized the ordinary Cissoid (a word from the Greek meaning "ivy") in finding two mean proportionals between given lengths a,b (i.e., finding x such that a, ax, ax^2, b form a geometric progression. This is the cube-root problem since $x^3 = \frac{b}{a}$). Generalizations follow. As early as 1689, J. C. Sturm, in his Mathesis Enucleata, gave a mechanical device for the construction of the Cissoid of Diocles.

1. DESCRIPTION: Given two curves $y = f_1(x)$, $y = f_2(x)$ and the fixed point 0. Let Q and R be the intersections of a variable line through 0 with the given curves. The locus of P on this secant such that

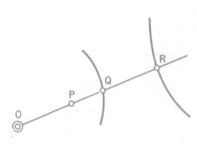

Fig. 23

$$OP = (OR) - (OQ) = QR$$

is the Cissoid of the two curves with respect to 0. If the two curves are a line and a circle, the ordinary family of Cissoids is generated. The discussion following is restricted to this family.

Let the two given curves be a fixed circle of radius a, center at K and passing through 0, and the line L perpendicular to OX at 2(a + b) distance from 0. The ordinary Cissoid is the locus of P on the variable secant through 0 such that OP = r = QR.

The generation may be effected by the intersection P of the secant OR and the circle of radius a tangent to L at R as this circle rolls upon L. (Fig. 24)

The curve has a cusp if b = 0 (the Cissoid of Diocles); a double point if the rolling circle passes between O and K. Its asymptote is the line L.

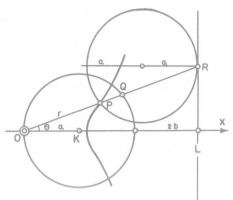

Fig. 24

2. EQUATIONS:

$$r = 2(a + b)\sec\theta - 2a\cos\theta. \qquad y^2 = \frac{x^2(2b - x)}{[x - 2(a+b)]}$$

$$\begin{cases} x = \dfrac{2\cdot[b + (a + b)t^2]}{(1 + t^2)} \\[2mm] y = \dfrac{2\cdot[bt + (a + b)t^3]}{(1 + t^2)} \end{cases}$$

(If b = 0: $r = 2a\cdot\sin\theta\tan\theta$; $y^2 = \dfrac{x^3}{(2a-x)}$, the Cissoid of Diocles).

3. METRICAL PROPERTIES:

Cissoid of Diocles: V(rev. about asymp.) $= 2\pi^2 a^3$

$\bar{x}$(area betw. curve and asymp.) $= \dfrac{5a}{3}$

A(area betw. curve and asymp.) $= \pi a^2$

4. GENERAL ITEMS:

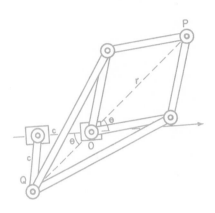

(a) A family of these Cissoids may be generated by the <u>Peaucellier cell</u> arrangement shown. Since $(OQ)(QP) = k^2 = 1$, $2c \cdot \cos \theta(2c \cdot \cos \theta + r) = 1$,

or

$$r = (\frac{1}{2c}) \sec \theta - 2c \cdot \cos \theta,$$

which, for $c < = > \frac{1}{2}$

has, respectively, <u>no loop</u>, <u>a cusp</u>, <u>a loop</u>.

Fig. 25

(b) The <u>Inverse</u> of the family in (a) is, if $r \cdot \rho = 1$, (center of inversion at O)

$$y^2 + x^2(1 - 4c^2) = 2cx,$$

an <u>Ellipse</u>, a <u>Parabola</u>, an <u>Hyperbola</u> if $c < = > \frac{1}{2}$, respectively. (See Conics, 17).

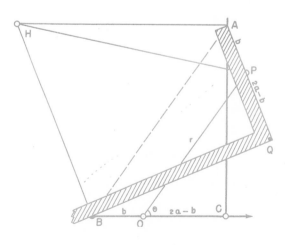

(c) Cissoids may be generated by the <u>carpenter's square</u> with right angle at Q (Newton). The fixed point A of the square moves along CA while the other edge of the square passes through B, a fixed point on the line BC perpendicular to

Fig. 26

AC. The path of P, a fixed point on AQ describes the
curve.

Let AP = OB = b, and BC = AQ = 2a, with O the origin
of coordinates. Then AB = 2a·sec θ and

$$r = 2a\cdot\sec\theta - 2b\cdot\cos\theta.$$

The point Q describes a Strophoid (See Strophoid 5e).

(d) <u>Tangent</u> <u>Construction</u>: (See Fig. 26) A has the
direction of the line CA while the point of the square
at B moves in the direction BQ. Normals to AC and BQ
at A and B respectively meet in H the center of rotation. HP is thus normal to the path of P.

(e) The Cissoid $y^2 = \dfrac{x^3}{(a - x)}$ is the <u>pedal</u> <u>of</u> <u>the</u>
<u>Parabola</u> $y^2 = -4ax$ with respect to its vertex.

(f) It is a special <u>Kieroid</u>.

(g) The Cissoid as a <u>roulette</u>: One of the curves is
the locus of the vertex of a parabola which rolls upon
an equal fixed one. The common tangent reflects the
fixed vertex into the position of the moving vertex.
The locus is thus a curve similar to the pedal with
respect to the vertex.

(h) The Cissoid of an algebraic curve and a line is
itself <u>algebraic</u>.

(i) The Cissoid of a line and a circle with respect to its center is the Conchoid of Nicomedes.

(j) The Strophoid is the Cissoid of a circle and a line through its center with respect to a point of the circle. The Cissoid of Diocles is used in the design of planing hulls (See Lord).

(k) The Cissoid of 2 concentric circles with respect to their center is a circle.

(l) The Cissoid of a pair of parallel lines is a line.

BIBLIOGRAPHY

Hilton, H.: Plane Algebraic Curves, Oxford (1932) 175, 203.
Wieleitner, H.: Spezielle ebene Kurven, Leipsig (1908) 37ff.
Salmon, G.: Higher Plane Curves, Dublin (1879) 182ff.
Niewenglowski, B.: Cours de Géométrie Analytique, Paris (1895) II, 115.
Lord, Lindsay: The Naval Architecture of Planing Hulls, Cornell Maritime Press (1946) 77.

CONCHOID

HISTORY: Nicomedes (about 225 BC) utilized the Conchoid (from the Greek meaning "shell-like") in finding two mean proportionals between two given lengths (the cube-root problem).

1. DESCRIPTION: Given a curve and a fixed point O. Points P_1 and P_2 are taken on a variable line through O at distances + k from the intersection of the line and curve. The locus of P_1 and P_2 is the Conchoid of the given curve with respect to O.

Fig. 27

The <u>Conchoid of Nicomedes</u> is the Conchoid of a Line.

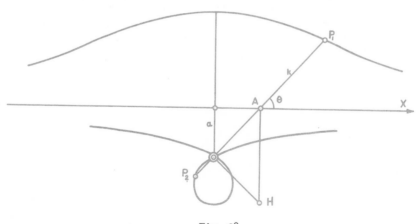

Fig. 28

The <u>Limacon</u> <u>of</u> <u>Pascal</u> is a Conchoid of a circle, with the fixed point upon the circle.

2. EQUATIONS:

General: Let the given curve be $r = f(\theta)$ and 0 be the origin. The Conchoid is

$$r = f(\theta) \pm k.$$

The <u>Conchoid</u> <u>of</u> <u>Nicomedes</u> (for the figure above) is:

$$r = a \cdot \csc \theta \pm k, \quad (x^2 + y^2)(y - a)^2 = k^2 y^2,$$

which has a <u>double point</u>, a <u>cusp,</u> or an <u>isolated point</u> if a < = > k, respectively.

3. METRICAL PROPERTIES:

4. GENERAL ITEMS:

(a) <u>Tangent Construction.</u> (See Fig. 28). The perpendicular to AX at A meets the perpendicular to OA at O in the point H, the center of rotation of any point of OA. Accordingly, HP$_1$ and HP$_2$ are normals to the curve.

(b) <u>The</u> <u>Trisection</u> <u>of</u> <u>an</u> <u>Angle</u> XOY by the marked ruler involves the Conchoid of Nicomedes. Let P and Q be the two marks on the ruler 2k units apart. Construct BC parallel to OX such that OB = k. Draw BA perpendicular to BC. Let P move along AB while the edge of the ruler passes through O. The point Q traces a Conchoid and when this point falls on BC the angle is trisected.

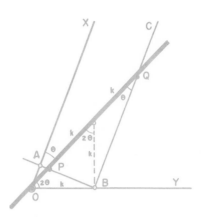

Fig. 29

(c) The Conchoid of Nicomedes is a special Kieroid.

BIBLIOGRAPHY

Mortiz, R. E.: Univ. of Washington Publications, (1923) [for Conchoids of $r = \cos(p/q)\theta$].
Hilton, H.: <u>Plane</u> <u>Algebraic</u> <u>Curves</u>, Oxford (1932).
Yates, R. C.: <u>The</u> <u>Trisection</u> <u>Problem</u>, West Point, N. Y. (1942)

CONES

1. DESCRIPTION: A cone is a ruled surface all of whose line elements pass through a fixed point called the vertex.

2. EQUATIONS: Given two surfaces $f(x,y,z) = 0$, $g(x,y,z) = 0$. The cone through their common curve with vertex V at (a,b,c) is found as follows.

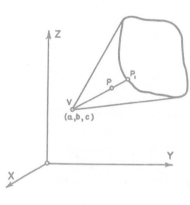

Fig. 30

Let $P_1:(x_1,y_1,z_1)$ be on the given curve and $P:(x,y,z)$ a point on the cone which lies collinear with V and P_1. Then

$$\boxed{\begin{aligned} x - a &= k(x_1 - a), \\ y - b &= k(y_1 - b), \\ z - c &= k(z_1 - c), \end{aligned}}$$ *

for all values of k.

Thus the curve

$$\begin{cases} f(x_1,y_1,z_1) = 0 \\ g(x_1,y_1,z_1) = 0 \end{cases}$$

produces the cone:

$$\begin{cases} f[\dfrac{(x - a)}{k} + a, \dfrac{(y - b)}{k} + b, \dfrac{(z - c)}{k} + c] = 0 \\ g[\dfrac{(x - a)}{k} + a, \dfrac{(y - b)}{k} + b, \dfrac{(z - c)}{k} + c] = 0 \end{cases}$$

Since this condition must exist for all values k, the elimination of k yields the rectangular equation of the cone.

---

* Thus any equation homogeneous in x,y,z is a cone with vertex at the origin.

3. EXAMPLES: The cone with vertex at the origin containing the curve

$$\begin{cases} x^2 + y^2 - 2z = 0 \\ z - 1 = 0 \end{cases} \text{is} \begin{cases} x^2 + y^2 - 2kz = 0 \\ z - k = 0 \end{cases} \text{or } \underline{x^2 + y^2 - 2z^2 = 0}.$$

The cone with vertex at the origin containing the curve

$$\begin{cases} x^2 - 2x + y^2 - 4y = 0 \\ z^2 - 4y = 0 \end{cases} \text{is} \begin{cases} x^2 - 2kx + y^2 - 4ky = 0 \\ z^2 - 4ky = 0 \end{cases} \text{or } \underline{2x^2y - xz^2 + 2y^3 - 2yz^2 = 0}.$$

The cone with vertex at $(1,2,3)$ containing the curve

$$\begin{cases} x^2 + y^2 - 2z = 0 \\ z - 4 = 0 \end{cases} \text{is} \begin{cases} \dfrac{[(x-1)^2 + (y-2)^2]}{k^2} + \dfrac{[2(x-1) + 4(y-2)]}{k} - \dfrac{2(z-3)}{k} - 1 = 0 \\ \dfrac{(z-3)}{k} - 1 = 0 \end{cases}$$

or $\underline{(x-1)^2 + (y-2)^2 + 2(x-1)(z-3) + 4(y-2)(z-3) - 3 \cdot (z-3)^2 = 0}.$

BIBLIOGRAPHY

Smith, Gale, Neelley: Analytic Geometry, Ginn (1938) 284.

CONICS

HISTORY: The Conics seem to have been discovered by
Menaechmus (a Greek, c.375-325 BC), tutor to Alexander the
Great. They were apparently conceived in an attempt to
solve the three famous problems of trisecting the angle,
duplicating the cube, and squaring the circle. Instead
of cutting a single fixed cone with a variable plane,
Menaechmus took a fixed intersecting plane and cones of
varying vertex angle, obtaining from those having angles
< = > 90° the Ellipse, Parabola, and Hyperbola respec-
tively. Apollonius is credited with the definition of
the plane locus given first below. The ingenious Pascal
announced his remarkable theorem on inscribed hexagons
in 1639 before the age of 16.

1. DESCRIPTION: A Conic is the locus of a point which
moves so that the ratio of its distance from a fixed
point (the focus) divided by its distance from a fixed
line (the directrix) is a constant (the eccentricity e),
all motion in the plane of focus and directrix (Apollonius). If e < , =, > 1, the locus is an Ellipse, a
Parabola, an Hyperbola respectively.

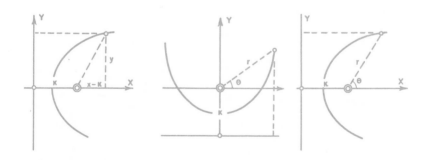

Fig. 31

$$y^2 + (1-e^2)x^2 - 2kx + k^2 = 0. \quad r = \frac{ek}{(1 \pm e \sin \theta)} \cdot \quad r = \frac{ek}{(1 \pm e \cos \theta)} \cdot$$

2. SECTIONS OF A CONE: Consider the right circular cone
of angle β cut by a plane
APFD which makes an angle
α with the base of the cone.
Let P be an arbitrarily
chosen point upon their
curve of intersection and
let a sphere be inscribed to
the cone touching the cutting plane at F. The element
through P touches the sphere
at B. Then

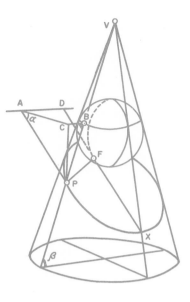

$$PF = PB.$$

Let ACBD be the plane containing the circle of intersection of cone and sphere.
Then if PC is perpendicular
to this plane,

$$PC = (PA)\sin\alpha = (PB)\sin\beta = (PF)\sin\beta,$$

or

$$\frac{(PF)}{(PA)} = \frac{\sin\alpha}{\sin\beta} = e,$$

Fig. 32

a constant as P varies (**α, β** constant). The curve of intersection is thus a conic according to the definition of
Apollonius. A focus and corresponding directrix are F
and AD, the intersection of the two planes.

NOTE: It is evident now that the three types of conics
may be had in either of two ways:

(A) By fixing the cone and varying the intersecting
plane (β constant and α arbitrary); or

(B) By fixing the plane and varying the right circular
cone (α constant and β arbitrary).

With either choice, the intersecting curve is

an <u>Ellipse</u> if α < β,
a <u>Parabola</u> if α = β ,
an <u>Hyperbola</u> if α > β .

3. PARTICULAR TYPE DEMONSTRATIONS:

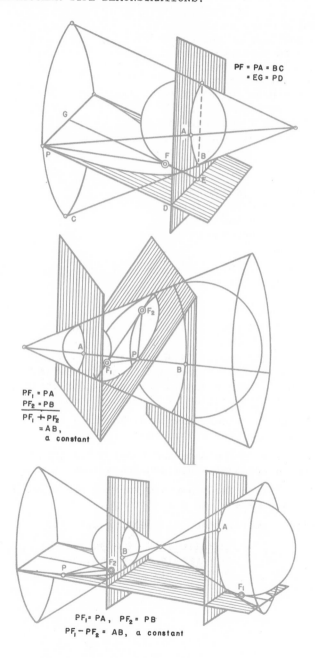

PF = PA = BC
= EG = PD

PF₁ = PA
PF₂ = PB
‾‾‾‾‾‾‾‾‾
PF₁ + PF₂
= AB,
a constant

PF₁ = PA, PF₂ = PB
PF₁ − PF₂ = AB, a constant

Fig. 33

It seems truly remarkable that these spheres, inscribed
to the cone and its cutting plane, should touch this
plane at the foci of the conic - and that the directrices
are the intersections of cutting plane and plane of the
intersection of cone and sphere.

4. THE DISCRIMINANT: Consider the general equation of
the Conic:

$$Ax^2 + 2Bxy + Cy^2 + 2Dx + 2Ey + F = 0$$

and the family of lines $y = mx$.

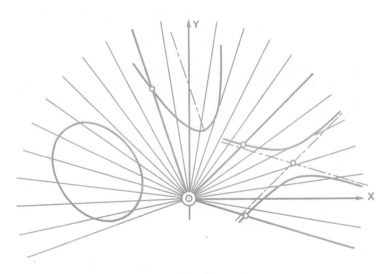

Fig. 34

This family meets the conic in points whose abscissas
are given by the form:

$$(A + 2Bm + Cm^2)x^2 + 2(D + Em)x + F = 0.$$

If there are lines of the family which cut the curve in one and only one point,* then

$$A + 2Bm + Cm^2 = 0 \quad \text{or} \quad m = \frac{-B \pm \sqrt{B^2 - AC}}{C}.$$

The <u>Parabola</u> is the conic for which <u>only one line</u> of the family cuts the curve just once. That is, for which:

$$B^2 - AC = 0.$$

The <u>Hyperbola</u> is the conic for which <u>two and only two lines</u> cut the curve just once. That is, for which:

$$B^2 - AC > 0.$$

The <u>Ellipse</u> is the conic for which <u>no line</u> of the family cuts the curve just once. That is, for which:

$$B^2 - AC < 0.$$

5. OPTICAL PROPERTY: A simple demonstration of this outstanding feature of the Conics is given here in the case of the Ellipse. Similar treatments may be presented for the Hyperbola and Parabola.

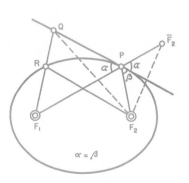

Fig. 35

The locus of points P for which $F_1P + F_2P = 2a$, a constant, is an Ellipse. Let the tangent to the curve be drawn at P. Now P is the only point of the tangent line for which $F_1P + F_2P$ is a minimum. For, consider any other point Q. Then

$$F_1Q + F_2Q > F_1R + F_2R = 2a = F_1P + F_2P.$$

But if $F_1P + F_2P$ is a minimum, P must be collinear with F_1 and $\bar{F}_2$, the reflection of F_2 in the

---

* A point of tangency here is counted algebraically as two points, the "point at ∞" is excluded.

tangent. Accordingly, since $\alpha = \beta$, the tangent bisects
the angle formed by the focal radii.

o. POLES AND POLARS: Consider the Conic:

$$Ax^2 + 2Bxy + Cy^2 + 2Dx + 2Ey + F = 0$$

and the point $P:(h,k)$.

The line (whose equation
has the form of a tangent
to the conic):

  $Ahx + B(hy + kx) + Cky$

  $+ D(x + h) + E(y + k)$

  $+ F = 0\ldots\ldots\ldots\ldots(1)$

is the polar of P with
respect to the conic and
P is its pole.

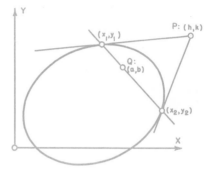

Fig. 36

   Let tangents be drawn
from P to the curve, meeting it in (x_1,y_1) and
(x_2,y_2). Their equations are satisfied by (h,k) thus:

$$Ahx_1 + B(hy_1 + kx_1) + Ckx_1 + D(x_1 + h) + E(y_1 + k) + F = 0$$

$$Ahx_2 + B(hy_2 + kx_2) + Ckx_2 + D(x_2 + k) + E(y_2 + k) + F = 0.$$

Evidently, the polar given by (1) contains these points
of tangency since its equation reduces to these identi
ties on replacing x,y by either x_1,y_1 or x_2,y_2. Thus,
if P is a point from which tangents may be drawn, its
polar is their chord of contact.

   Let (a,b) be a point on the polar of P. Then

$$Aha + B(hb + ka) + \ldots + F = 0.$$

This expresses also the condition that the polar of
(a,b) passes through (h,k). Thus

<u>If P lies on the polar of Q, then Q lies on the polar</u> of P.

In other words, if a point move on a fixed line, its polar passes through a fixed point, and conversely.

Note that the location of P relative to the conic does not affect the reality of its polar. Note also that if P lies on the conic, its polar is the tangent at P.

7. HARMONIC SECTION: Let the line through P_2 meet the conic in Q_1, Q_2 and its polar in P_1. These four points form an harmonic set and

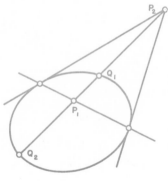

Fig. 37

$$\frac{(P_1Q_1)}{(Q_1P_2)} = \frac{(Q_2P_1)}{(Q_2P_2)} \text{ , i.e., } Q_1$$

and Q_2 divide the segment P_1P_2 internally and externally in the same ratio, and vice versa. In other words, given the conic and a fixed point P_2: A variable line through P_2 meets the conic in Q_1, Q_2. The locus of P_1 which, with P_2, divides Q_1Q_2 harmonically is the polar of P_2.

The segments P_2Q_1, P_2P_1, P_2Q_2 are in harmonic progression. That is:

$$\frac{2}{(P_2P_1)} = \frac{1}{(P_2Q_1)} + \frac{1}{(P_2Q_2)}$$

8. THE POLAR OF P PASSES THROUGH R AND S, THE INTERSEC-
TIONS OF THE CROSS-JOINS OF SECANTS THROUGH P. (Fig. 38a)

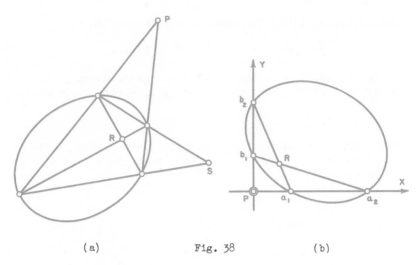

(a)   Fig. 38   (b)

Let the two arbitrary secants be axes of reference (not
necessarily rectangular) and let the conic (Fig. 38b)

$$Ax^2 + 2Bxy + Cy^2 + 2Dx + 2Ey + F = 0$$

have intercepts a_1, a_2; b_1, b_2 given as the roots of

$$Ax^2 + 2Dx + F = 0 \quad \text{and} \quad Cy^2 + 2Ey + F = 0.$$

From these

$$\frac{1}{a_1} + \frac{1}{a_2} = -\frac{2D}{F} \quad \text{or} \quad D = \left(-\frac{F}{2}\right)\left(\frac{1}{a_1} + \frac{1}{a_2}\right),$$

$$\frac{1}{b_1} + \frac{1}{b_2} = -\frac{2E}{F} \quad \text{or} \quad E = \left(-\frac{F}{2}\right)\left(\frac{1}{b_1} + \frac{1}{b_2}\right).$$

Now the polar of $P(0,0)$ is $Dx + Ey + F = 0$
or

$$x\left(\frac{1}{a_1} + \frac{1}{a_2}\right) + y\left(\frac{1}{b_1} + \frac{1}{b_2}\right) - 2 = 0.$$

The cross-joins are:

$$\frac{x}{a_1} + \frac{y}{b_2} = 1 \quad \text{and} \quad \frac{x}{a_2} + \frac{y}{b_1} = 1.$$

The family of lines through their intersection R:

$$\frac{x}{a_1} + \frac{y}{b_2} - 1 + \lambda(\frac{x}{a_2} + \frac{y}{b_1} - 1) = 0.$$

contains, for $\lambda = 1$, the polar of P. Accordingly, the polar of P passes through R, and by inference, through S.

This affords a simple and classical construction by the straightedge alone of the tangents to a conic from a point P:

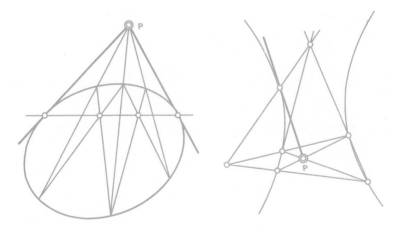

Fig. 39

Draw arbitrary secants from P and, by the intersections of their cross-joins, establish the polar of P. This polar meets the conic in the points of tangency.

9. PASCAL'S THEOREM:

One of the most far reaching and productive theorems in all of geometry is concerned with hexagons inscribed to conics. Let the vertices of the hexagon be numbered arbitrarily*

1, 2, 3, 1', 2', 3'. <u>The intersections</u> <u>X</u>, <u>Y</u>, <u>Z</u> <u>of</u> <u>the joins</u> (1,2';1'2) (1,3';1',3) (2,3';2',3) <u>are</u> <u>collinear</u>, <u>and</u> <u>conversely</u>. Apparently simple in character, it nevertheless has over 400 corollaries important to the structure of synthetic geometry. Several of these follow.

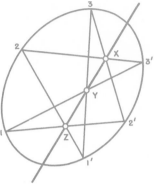

Fig. 40

By renumbering, many such Pascal lines correspond to a single inscribed hexagon.

10. POINTWISE CONSTRUCTION OF A CONIC DETERMINED BY FIVE
GIVEN POINTS:

Let the five points be numbered 1,2,3,1',2'. Draw an

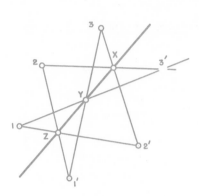

arbitrary line through 1
which would meet the conic
in the required point 3'.
Establish the two points
Y,Z and the Pascal line.
This meets 2'3 in X and
finally 2,X meets the
arbitrary line through 1
in 3'. Further points are
located in the same way.

Fig. 41

11. CONSTRUCTION OF TANGENTS TO A CONIC GIVEN ONLY BY
FIVE POINTS:

In labelling the points, consider 1 and 3' as having

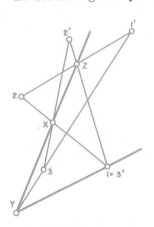

merged so that the line 1,3' is
the tangent. Points X, Z are
determined and the Pascal line
drawn to meet 1',3 in Y. The
line from Y to the point 1=3'
is the required tangent. The
tangent at any other point,
determined as in (10), is constructed in like fashion.

Fig. 42

12. INSCRIBED QUADRILATERALS: The pairs of tangents at
opposite vertices, to-
gether with the oppo-
site sides, of quadri-
laterals inscribed to
a conic meet in four
collinear points.
This is recognized as
a special case of the
inscribed hexagon
theorem of Pascal.

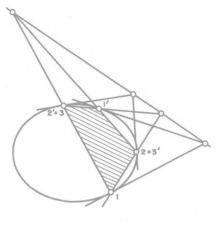

Fig. 43

13. INSCRIBED TRIANGLES: Further restriction on the
Pascal hexagon pro-
duces a theorem on
inscribed triangles.
For such triangles,
the tangents at the
vertices meet their
opposite sides in
three collinear
points.

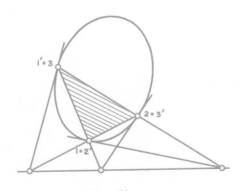

Fig. 44

14. AEROPLANE DESIGN: The construction of elliptical
sections at right
angles to the center
line of a fuselage is
essentially as follows.
Construct the conic
given three points P_1,
P_2, P_3 and the tangents
at two of them. To ob-
tain other points Q on
the conic, draw an
arbitrary Pascal line
through X, the inter-
section of the given
tangents, meeting P_1P_2
in Y; P_1P_3 in Z. Then
YP_3 and ZP_2 meet in Q.

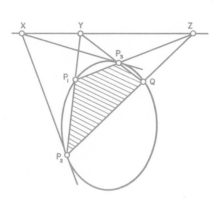

Fig. 45

15. DUALITY: The Principle of Duality, inherently fundamental in the theory of Pro-
jective Geometry, affords a
corresponding theorem for
each of the foregoing.
Pascal's Theorem (1639)
dualizes into the theorem
of Brianchon (1806):

If a hexagon circumscribe
a conic, the three joins of
the opposite vertices are
concurrent. (This is apparent
on polarizing the Pascal
hexagon.)

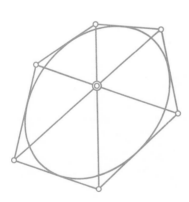

Fig. 46

16. CONSTRUCTION AND GENERATION: (See also Sketching 2.)
The following are a few selected from many. Explanations
are given only where necessary.

(a) <u>String</u> <u>Methods</u>:

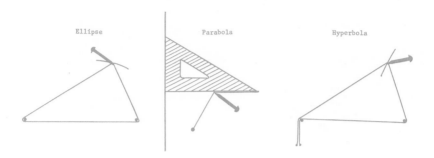

Fig. 47

(b) <u>Point-wise</u> <u>Construction</u>:

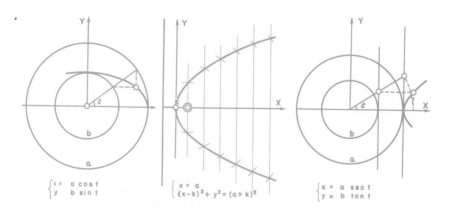

Fig. 48

CONICS

(c) <u>Two</u> <u>Envelopes</u>:

(i) A ray is drawn from the fixed point F to the fixed circle or line. At this point of intersection a

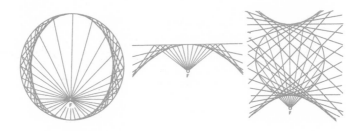

Fig. 49

line is drawn perpendicular to the ray. The envelope of this latter line is a conic* (See Pedals.)

(ii) The fixed point F of a sheet of paper is folded over upon the fixed circle or line. The <u>crease</u>

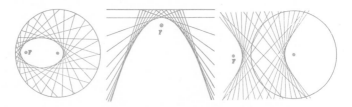

Fig. 50

so formed envelopes a conic. (See Envelopes.) (Use wax paper.) (Note that i and ii are equivalent.)

---

* This is a Glissette: the envelope of one side of a Carpenter's square whose corner moves along a circle while its other leg passes through a fixed point. See Cissoid 4, and <u>Glissettes</u> 6e.

(d) <u>Newton's</u> <u>Method</u>: Based upon the idea of two projective pencils, the
following is due to
Newton. Two angles of
constant magnitudes
have vertices fixed
at A and B. A point
of intersection P of
two of their sides
moves along a fixed
line. The point of
intersection Q of
their other two
sides describes a
conic through A and
B.

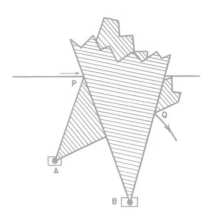

Fig. 51

17. LINKAGE DESCRIPTION: The following is selected from
a variety of such
mechanisms (see TOOLS).

For the 3-bar linkage
shown, forming a vari-
able trapezoid:

$AB = CD = 2a$; $AC = BD = 2b$;
$a > b$;

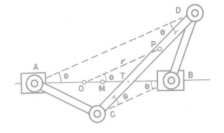

$(AD)(BC) = 4(a^2 - b^2)$.

A point P of CD is
selected and $OP = r$
drawn parallel to AD   Fig. 52
and BC. OP will remain
parallel to these lines and so O is a fixed point.

Let $OM = c$, $MT = z$, where M is the midpoint of AB.
Then

$$AD = 2(AT)\cos\,\theta = 2(a + z)\cos\,\theta,$$
$$BC = 2(BT)\cos\,\theta = 2(a - z)\cos\,\theta.$$

Their product produces:

$$(a^2 - z^2)\cos^2\theta = a^2 - b^2.$$

Combining this with $r = 2(c + z)\cos\,\theta$ there results

$$(\frac{r}{2} - c\cdot\cos\,\theta)^2 = b^2 - a^2\sin^2\theta$$

as the polar equation of the path of P. In rectangular coordinates these curves are degenerate sextics, each composed of a circle and a curve resembling the figure ∞.

If now an inversor OEPFP' be attached as shown in Fig. 53 so that

$$r\cdot\rho = 2k, \quad \text{where } \rho = OP',$$

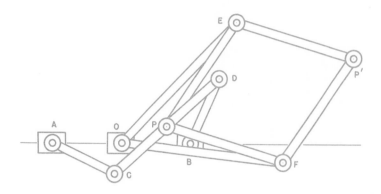

Fig. 53

the inverse of this set of curves (the locus of P') is:

$$(k - c\cdot\rho\cdot\cos\,\theta)^2 = b^2 - a^2\cdot\rho^2\cdot\sin^2\theta,$$

or, in rectangular coordinates:

$$(a^2 - b^2)y^2 - (b^2 - c^2)x^2 - 2c\cdot k\cdot x + k^2 = 0$$

a _conic_. Since a > b, the type depends upon the relative value of c; that is, upon the position of the selected point P:

An <u>Ellipse</u>   if   c > b,

A <u>Parabola</u>   if   c = b,

An <u>Hyperbola</u> if   c < b.

(For an alternate linkage, see <u>Cissoid</u>, 4.)

18. RADIUS OF CURVATURE:

For any curve in rectangular coordinates,

$$\left| R \right| = \left| \frac{(1 + y'^2)^{3/2}}{y''} \right| \quad \text{and} \quad N^2 = y^2(1 + y'^2).$$

Thus

$$\left| R \right| = \left| \frac{N^3}{y^3 y''} \right| .$$

The conic $y^2 = 2Ax + Bx^2$, $B > -1$, where A is the semi-latus rectum, is an Ellipse if $B < 0$, a Parabola if $B = 0$, an Hyperbola if $B > 0$. Here

$$yy' = A + Bx, \quad yy'' + y'^2 = B, \quad \text{and} \quad y^3 y'' + y^2 y'^2 = By^2.$$

Thus
$$y^3 y'' = By^2 - (A + Bx)^2 = -A^2$$

and
$$\left| R \right| = \left| \frac{N^3}{A^2} \right| .$$

19. PROJECTION OF NORMAL LENGTH UPON A FOCAL RADIUS:

Consider the conics

$$\rho_1(1 - e \cos \theta) = A, \quad (A = \text{semi-latus rectum}).$$

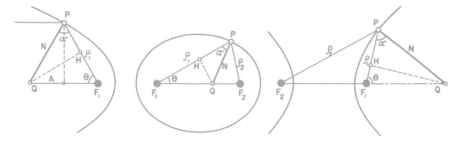

Fig. 54

Since the normal at P bisects the angle between the focal radii, we have for the central conics:

$$\frac{F_2 Q}{F_1 Q} = \frac{\rho_2}{\rho_1}$$

or, adding 1 to each side of the equation for the Ellipse, subtracting 1 from each side for the Hyperbola:

$$\frac{2c}{F_1 Q} = \frac{2a}{\rho_1} \ .$$

That is

$$\boxed{F_1 Q = e \cdot \rho_1 \ .}$$

Now if H be the foot of the perpendicular from Q upon a focal radius,

$$F_1 H = e\rho_1 \cdot \cos \theta$$

and

$$PH = \rho_1 - e\rho_1 \cdot \cos \theta = A = N \cdot \cos \alpha.$$

For the Parabola, the angles at P and Q are each equal to α and $F_1 Q = \rho_1$. Thus

$$PH = \rho_1 - \rho_1 \cdot \cos \theta = A = N \cdot \cos \alpha.$$

Accordingly,

The projection of the Normal Length upon a focal radius is constant and equal to the semi-latus rectum.

20. CENTER OF CURVATURE:

Since $\cos \alpha = \dfrac{A}{N}$, from (19),

   and $\left| R \right| = \left| \dfrac{N^3}{A^2} \right|$, from (18),

we have

                 $\left| R \right| = N \cdot \sec^2 \alpha.$

Thus to locate the center
of curvature, C, draw the
perpendicular to the
normal at Q meeting a
focal radius at K. Draw
the perpendicular at K
to this focal radius
meeting the normal in C.
(For the Evolutes of the
Conics, see Evolutes, 4.)
(In connection see Keill.)

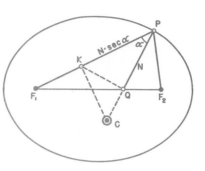

Fig. 55

BIBLIOGRAPHY

Baker, W. M.: Algebraic Geometry, Bell and Sons (1906)
    313.
Brink, R. W.: A First Year of College Mathematics,
    Appleton Century (1937).
Candy, A. L.: Analytic Geometry, D. C. Heath (1900) 155.
Graham, John and Cooley: Analytic Geometry, Prentice-
    Hall (1936) 207.
Niewenglowski, B.: Cours de Géométrie Analytique, Paris
    (1895).
Salmon, G.: Conic Sections, Longmans, Green (1900).
Sanger, R. G.: Synthetic Projective Geometry, McGraw
    Hill (1939) 66.
Winger, R. M.: Projective Geometry, D. C. Heath (1923)
    112.
Yates, R. C.: Geometrical Tools, Educational Publishers,
    St. Louis (1949) 174, 180.
Keill, J.: Philosophical Transactions, XXVI (1708-9)
    177-8.

CUBIC PARABOLA

HISTORY: Studied particularly by Newton and Leibnitz (1675) who sought a curve whose subnormal is inversely proportional to its ordinate. Monge used the Parabola $y = x^3$ in 1815 to solve every cubic of the form $x^3 + hx + k = 0$.

1. DESCRIPTION: The curve is defined by the equation:

$$y = Ax^3 + Bx^2 + Cx + D = A(x - a)(x^2 + bx + c).$$

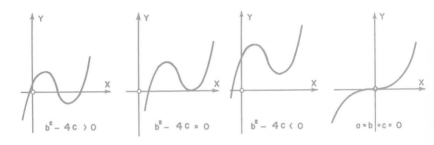

Fig. 56

2. GENERAL ITEMS:

   (a) The Cubic Parabola has <u>max-min. points</u> only if $B^2 - 3AC > 0$.

   (b) Its <u>flex point</u> is at $x = \dfrac{-B}{3A}$ (a translation of the y-axis by this amount removes the square term and thus selects the mean of the roots as the origin).

   (c) The curve is <u>symmetrical</u> with respect to its flex point (see b.).

   (d) It is a special case of the <u>Pearls of Sluze</u>.

   (e) It is used extensively as a <u>transition curve</u> in railroad engineering.

(f) It is continuous for all values of x, with no asymptotes, cusps, or double points.

(g) The Evolute of $a^2 y = x^3$ is

$$3a^2(x^2 - \frac{9}{125}y^2)^2 + \frac{128}{125}(\frac{2}{5}\,a^2 - \frac{9}{2}\,xy)(\frac{1}{5}\,a^4 - \frac{3}{2}\,a^2 xy - \frac{243}{400}\,y^4) = 0$$

(h) For $3a^2 y = x^3$, $R = \dfrac{(a^4 + x^4)^{\frac{3}{2}}}{2a^4 x}$

(i) <u>Graphical</u> <u>and</u> <u>Mechanical</u> Solutions:

1. Replace $x^3 + hx + k = 0$ by the system:

$$\begin{cases} y = x^3 \\ y + hx + k = 0, \end{cases}$$

the abscissas of whose intersections are roots of the given equation. Only one Cubic Parabola need be drawn for all cubics, but for each cubic there is a particular line.

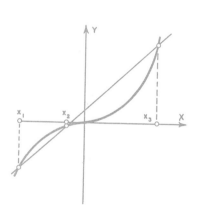

Fig. 57

2. Reduce the given cubic $x_1{}^3 + hx_1 + k = 0$ by means of the rational transformation $x_1 = \dfrac{k}{h} \cdot x$ to the form

$$x^3 + m(x + 1) = 0 \quad \text{in which } m = \frac{h^3}{k^2}. \,^*$$

---

*The <u>discriminant</u> (the square of the product of the differences of the roots taken in pairs) of this cubic is:

$$\Delta = -m^2(27 + 4m).$$

Thus the roots are real and unequal if $m < -\frac{27}{4}$; two are complex if $m > -\frac{27}{4}$; and two or more are equal if $m = 0$ or $m = -\frac{27}{4}$.

These regions of the plane (or ranges of m) are separated by the line through (-1,0) tangent to the curve as shown.

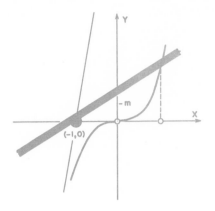

Fig. 58

This may be replaced by the system $\left\{ y=x^3,\ y+m(x+1)=0 \right\}$. Since the solution of each cubic here requires only the determination of a particular <u>slope</u>, a straightedge may be attached to the point $(-1,0)$ with the y-axis accommodating the quantity <u>m</u>.

(j) <u>Trisection</u> <u>of</u> <u>the</u> <u>Angle</u>:

Given the angle AOB = 3θ. If OA be the radius of the unit circle, then the projection <u>a</u> is $\cos 3\theta$. It is proposed to find $\cos \theta$ and thus θ itself.

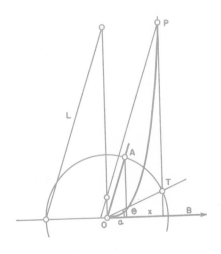

Fig. 59

Since
$$\cos 3\theta = 4 \cos^3\theta - 3 \cos \theta,$$
we have, in setting
$x = \cos \theta$: $4x^3 - 3x - a = 0$
or the equivalent system:
$y = 4x^3$, $y - 3x - a = 0$.
Thus, for trisection of 3θ, draw the line through $(0,a)$ parallel to the fixed line L of slope 3. This meets the curve $y = 4x^3$ at P. The line from P perpendicular to

OB meets the unit circle in T and determines the required
distance x. The trisecting line is OT.

BIBLIOGRAPHY

Yates, R. C.: Geometrical Tools, Educational Publishers,
St. Louis (1949).
Yates, R. C.: The Trisection Problem, West Point, N. Y.
(1942).

CURVATURE

1. DEFINITION: Curvature is a measure of the rate of change of the angle of inclination of the tangent with respect to the arc length. Precisely,

$$K = \frac{d\varphi}{ds} . \qquad\qquad R = \frac{1}{K} .$$

At a <u>maximum</u> or <u>minimum</u> <u>point</u> K = y" (or ∞, 0); at a <u>flex</u> if y" is continuous, K = 0 (or ∞); at a <u>cusp</u>, R = 0. (See Evolutes).

2. OSCULATING CIRCLE:

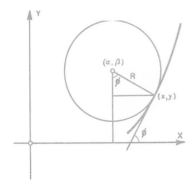

Fig. 60

The osculating circle of a curve is the circle having (x,y), y' and y" in common with the curve. That is, the relations:

$$(x - \alpha)^2 + (y - \beta)^2 = r^2$$

$$(x - \alpha) + (y - \beta)y' = 0$$

$$(1 + y'^2) + (y - \beta)y" = 0$$

must subsist for values of x,y,y',y" belonging to the curve. These conditions give:

$$r = R, \quad \alpha = x - R \cdot \sin \varphi, \quad \beta = y + R \cdot \cos \varphi,$$

where φ is the tangential angle. This is also called the <u>Circle</u> <u>of</u> <u>Curvature</u>.

3. CURVATURE AT THE ORIGIN (Newton): We consider only rational algebraic curves having the x-axis as a tangent at the origin. Let A be the center of a circle tangent to the curve at 0 and intersecting the curve again at P:(x,y). As P approaches 0, the circle approaches the osculating circle. Now BP = x is a mean

proportional between OB = y

and BC = 2R - y, where

AO = R. That is,

$$2R - y = \frac{x^2}{y} \text{ , and}$$

$$R_0 = \underset{\substack{P \to 0}}{\text{Limit}} R = \underset{\substack{x \to 0 \\ y \to 0}}{\text{Limit}} (\frac{x^2}{2y}).$$

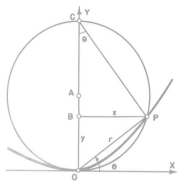

Fig. 61

<u>Examples</u>: The Parabola $2y = x^2$ has $R_0 = 1$.

The Cubic $y^2 = x^3$ or $\frac{x^2}{2y} = \sqrt{\frac{x}{2}}$ has $R_0 = 0$.

The Quintic $y^2 = x^5$ or $\frac{x^2}{2y} = \frac{1}{2\sqrt{x}}$ has $R_0 = \infty$.

Generally, curvature at the origin is independent of all coefficients except those of y and x^2.

If the curve be given in polar coordinates, through the pole and tangent to the polar axis, there is in like fashion (see Fig. 61):

$$2R \cdot \sin \theta = r \qquad \text{or} \qquad R = \frac{r}{2 \sin \theta} \text{ ;}$$

$$R_0 = \underset{\theta \to 0}{\text{Limit}} (\frac{r}{2 \sin \theta}) = \underset{\theta \to 0}{\text{Limit}} (\frac{r}{2\theta}).$$

<u>Examples</u>: The Circle

$$r = a \cdot \sin \theta \text{ or } \frac{r}{2\theta} = \frac{a(\sin \theta)}{2\theta} \text{ has } R_0 = \frac{a}{2} \text{ .}$$

The Cardioid

$$r = 1 - \cos \theta \text{ or } \frac{r}{2\theta} = \frac{(1 - \cos \theta)}{2\theta} \text{ has } R_0 = 0.$$

4. CURVATURE IN VARIOUS COORDINATE SYSTEMS:

$$R^2 = \frac{(1 + y'^2)^3}{y'^2} .$$

$$K^2 = (\frac{d^2x}{ds^2})^2 + (\frac{d^2y}{ds^2})^2 .$$

$$R_0 = \text{Limit } (\frac{x^2}{2y}) .$$
$$\quad x \to 0$$
$$\quad y \to 0$$

$$R^2 = \frac{(\dot{x}^2 + \dot{y}^2)^3}{(\dot{x}\ddot{y} - \ddot{x}\dot{y})^2} ,$$

[where the curve is
$x = x(t)$, $y = y(t)$ and

$. \equiv \frac{d}{dt}$].

$R = \frac{v^2}{a_n}$, where v, a_n are
magnitudes of velocity and
normal acceleration of a
moving point.

$$R = ds/d\varphi .$$

$$R = r(\frac{dr}{dp})$$

$$R = p + \frac{d^2p}{d\varphi^2} .$$

$$R^2 = \frac{(r^2 + r'^2)^3}{(r^2 + 2r'^2 - rr'')^2} \quad \text{(polar coords.)}$$

$$R^2 = \frac{(f_x^2 + f_y^2)^3}{(f_{xx}f_y^2 - 2f_{xy}f_xf_y + f_{yy}f_x^2)^2} ,$$

[where the curve is $f(x,y) = 0$].

$$R^2 = \frac{N^3}{y^3 \cdot y''} , \quad \text{where}$$

$$N^2 = y^2(1 + y'^2)$$

(See Conics, 18).

5. CURVATURE AT A SINGULAR POINT:

At a singular point of a curve $f(x,y) = 0$, $f_x = f_y = 0$. The character of the point is disclosed by the form:

$$F \equiv f_{xy}^2 - f_{xx}f_{yy}.$$

That is, if $F < 0$ there is an isolated point, if $F = 0$, a cusp, if $F > 0$, a node. The curvature at such a point (excluding the case $F < 0$) is determined by the usual $K \equiv \frac{y''}{(1 + y'^2)^{3/2}}$ after y' and y'' have been evaluated. The slopes y' may be determined (except when y' does not exist) from the indeterminate form $\frac{-f_x}{f_y}$ by the appropriate process involving differentiation.

6. CURVATURE FOR VARIOUS CURVES:

CURVES	EQUATION	R
Rect. Hyperbola	$r^2 \sin 2\theta = 2k^2$	$\dfrac{r^3}{2k^2}$
Catenary	$y^2 = c^2 + s^2$	$\dfrac{y^2}{c} = c\cdot\sec^2\varphi$ (See construction under Catenary)
Cycloid	$s = \sqrt{8ay}$	$4a\sqrt{1 - \dfrac{y}{2a}}$ (See construction under Cycloid)
	$x = a(t - \sin t)$ $y = a(1 - \cos t)$	$-4a\cdot\sin\left(\dfrac{t}{2}\right)$
Tractrix	$s = c\cdot\ln \sec \varphi$	$c\cdot\tan \varphi$
Equiangular Spiral	$s = a(e^{m\varphi} - 1)$	$ma\cdot e^{m\varphi}$
Lemniscate	$r^3 = a^2 p$	$\dfrac{a^2}{3r}$ (See construction under Lemniscate)
Ellipse	$a^2 + b^2 - r^2 = \dfrac{a^2 b^2}{p^2}$	$\dfrac{a^2 b^2}{p^3}$
Sinusoidal Spirals	$r^n = a^n \cos n\theta$	$\dfrac{a^n}{(n+1)r^{n-1}} = \dfrac{r^2}{(n+1)p}$
Astroid	$x^{\frac{2}{3}} + y^{\frac{2}{3}} = a^{\frac{2}{3}}$	$3(axy)^{1/3}$
Epi- and Hypo-cycloids	$p = a \sin b\varphi$	$a(1-b^2)\sin b\varphi = (1-b^2)\cdot p$

7. GENERAL ITEMS:

(a) Osculating circles at two corresponding points of inverse curves are inverse to each other.

(b) If R and R' be radii of curvature of a curve and its pedal at corresponding points:

$$R'(2r^2 - p\cdot R) = r^3.$$

CURVATURE

(c) The curve $y = x^n$ is useful in discussing curvature. Consider at the origin the cases for n rational, when $n < = > 2$. (See Evolutes.)

(d) For a parabola, R is twice the length of the normal intercepted by the curve and its directrix.

BIBLIOGRAPHY

Edwards, J.: <u>Calculus</u>, Macmillan (1892) 252.
Salmon, G.: <u>Higher Plane Curves</u>, Dublin (1879) 84.

CYCLOID

HISTORY: Apparently first conceived by Mersenne and Galileo Galilei in 1599 and studied by Roberval, Descartes, Pascal, Wallis, the Bernoullis and others. It enters naturally into a variety of situations and is justly celebrated. (See 4b and 4f.)

1. DESCRIPTION: The Cycloid is the path of a point of a circle rolling upon a fixed line (a roulette). The Prolate and Curtate Cycloids are formed if P is not on the circle but rigidly attached to it. For a point-wise

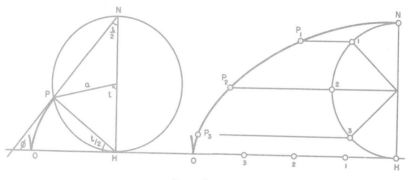

Fig. 62

construction, divide the interval OH (= πa) and the semicircle NH into an equal number of parts: 1, 2, 3, etc. Lay off $1P_1$ = H1, $2P_2$ = H2, etc., as shown.

2. EQUATIONS:

$$\begin{cases} x = a(t - \sin t) \\ y = a(1 - \cos t) = 2a \cdot \sin^2(\frac{t}{2}). \end{cases}$$

$s = 4a.\sin \emptyset$
(measured from top
of arch).

$R^2 + s^2 = 16a^2.$

3. METRICAL PROPERTIES:

(a) $\varphi = \dfrac{(\pi - t)}{2}$.

(b) $L_{(one\ arch)} = 8a$ (since $R_0 = 0$, $R_N = 4a$) (Sir Christopher Wren, 1658).

(c) $y' = \cot(\dfrac{t}{2})$ (since H is instantaneous center of rotation of P. Thus the tangent at P passes through N) (Descartes).

(d) $R = 4a \cdot \cos \phi = 4a \cdot \sin(\dfrac{t}{2}) = 2$ (PH) $= 2$(Normal).

(e) $s = 4a \cdot \cos(\dfrac{t}{2}) = 2$(NP).

(f) $A_{(one\ arch)} = 3\pi a^2$ (Roberval 1634, Galileo approximated this result in 1599 by carefully weighing pieces of paper cut into the shapes of a cycloidal arch and the generating circle).

4. GENERAL ITEMS:

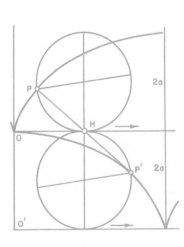

(a) Its evolute is an equal Cycloid. (Huygens 1673.) (Since $s = 4a \cdot \sin \phi$, $\sigma = 4a \cdot \cos\phi = 4a \cdot \sin\beta$) $R = PP'$ (the reflected circle rolls along the horizontal through O'. P' describes the evolute cycloid. One curve is thus an involute (or the evolute) of the other. (See Evolutes, 7.)

Fig. 63

(b) Since $s = 4a \cdot \cos(\frac{t}{2})$, $\frac{ds}{dt} = -2a \cdot \sin(\frac{t}{2}) = \sqrt{2ay}$.

(c) A Tautochrone: The problem of the Tautochrone is the determination of the type of curve along which a particle moves, subject to a specified force, to arrive at a given point in the same time interval no matter from what initial point it starts. The following was first demonstrated by Huygens in 1673, then by Newton in 1687, and later discussed by Jean Bernoulli, Euler, and Lagrange.

A particle P is confined in a vertical plane to a curve $s = f(\varphi)$ under the influence of gravity:

$$m\ddot{s} = -mg \cdot \sin \varphi.$$

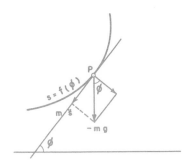

Fig. 64

If the particle is to produce harmonic motion: $m\ddot{s} = -k^2 s$, then

$$s = (\frac{mg}{k^2})\sin \varphi,$$

that is, the curve of restraint must be a cycloid, generated by a circle of radius $\frac{mg}{4k^2}$. The period of this motion is 2π, a period which is independent of the amplitude. Thus two balls (particles) of the same mass, falling on a cycloidal arc from different heights, will reach the lowest point at the same instant.

Since the evolute (or an involute) of a cycloid
is an equal cycloid,

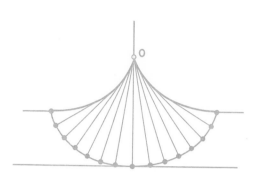

a bob B may be sup-
ported at O to de-
scribe cycloidal
motion. The period
of vibration of the
pendulum (under no
resistance) would
be constant for all
amplitudes and thus
the swings would

Fig. 65

count equal time intervals. Clocks designed upon this
principle were short lived.

(d) <u>A</u> <u>Brachistochrone</u>. First proposed by Jean
Bernoulli in 1696, the problem of the Brachistochrone
is the determination of the path along which a particle moves from one point in a plane to another, sub-

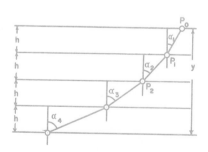

ject to a specified
force, in the short-
est time. The fol-
lowing discussion
is essentially the
solution given by
Jacques Bernoulli.
Solutions were also
presented by Leibnitz,

Fig. 66

Newton, and l'Hospital.

For a body falling under gravity along any curve
of restraint: $\ddot{y} = g$, $\dot{y} = gt$, $y = \dfrac{gt^2}{2}$ or $t = \sqrt{\dfrac{2y}{g}}$.
At any instant, the velocity of fall is

$$\dot{y} = g \cdot \sqrt{\frac{2y}{g}} = \sqrt{2gy} \ .$$

Let the medium through which the particle falls have
uniform density. At any depth y, $v = \sqrt{2gy}$. Let
theoretical layers of the medium be of infinitesimal
depth and assume that the velocity of the particle
changes at the surface of each layer. If it is to
pass from P_0 to P_1 to P_2 ... in shortest time, then
according to the law of refraction:

$$\frac{\sin \alpha_1}{\sqrt{2gh}} = \frac{\sin \alpha_2}{\sqrt{4gh}} = \frac{\sin \alpha_3}{\sqrt{6gh}} = \ \cdots$$

Thus the curve of descent, (the limit of the polygon
as h approaches zero and the number of layers increases
accordingly), is such that (Fig. 67):

$$\sin \alpha = k \cdot \sqrt{y} \quad \text{or} \quad \cos^2\theta = k^2 y,$$

an equation that may be iden-

tified as that of a Cycloid.

(e) The parallel projection

of a cylindrical helix onto a

plane perpendicular to its

axis is a Cycloid, prolate,

curtate, or ordinary. (Mon-

tucla, 1799; Guillery, 1847.)

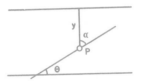

Fig. 67

(f) The Catacaustic of a cycloidal arch for a set of
parallel rays perpendicular to its base is composed of
two Cycloidal arches. (Jean Bernoulli 1692.)

(g) The isoptic curve of a Cycloid is a Curtate or
Prolate Cycloid (de La Hire 1704).

(h) Its radial curve is a Circle.

(i) It is frequently found desirable to design the
face and flank of teeth in rack gears as Cycloids.
(Fig. 68).

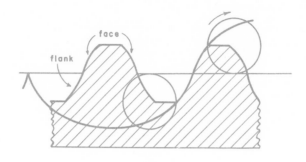

Fig. 68

BIBLIOGRAPHY

Edwards, J.: <u>Calculus</u>, Macmillan (1892) 337.
<u>Encyclopaedia</u> <u>Britannica</u>: 14th Ed. under "Curves,
    Special".
Gunther, S.: <u>Bibl</u>. <u>Math</u>. (2) v1, p.8.
Keown and Faires, <u>Mechanism</u>, McGraw Hill (1931) 139.
Salmon, G.: <u>Higher</u> <u>Plane</u> <u>Curves</u>, Dublin (1879) 275.
Webster, A.G.: <u>Dynamics</u> <u>of</u> <u>a</u> <u>Particle</u>, Leipsig (1912) 77.
Wolffing, E.: <u>Bibl</u>. <u>Math</u>. (3) v2,p.235.

DELTOID

HISTORY: Conceived by Euler in 1745 in connection with a study of caustic curves.

1. DESCRIPTION: The Deltoid is· a 3-cusped Hypocycloid. The rolling circle may be either one-third (a = 3b) or two-thirds (2a = 3b) as large as the fixed circle.

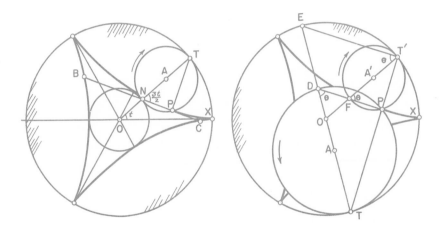

Fig. 69

For the double generation, consider the right-hand figure. Here $OE = OT = a$, $AD = AT = \dfrac{2a}{3}$, where 0 is the center of the fixed circle and A that of the rolling circle which carries the tracing point P. Draw TP to T', T'E, PD and T'0 meeting in F. Draw the circumcircle of F, P, and T' with center at A'. This circle is tangent to the fixed circle at T' since angle $FPT' = \dfrac{\pi}{2}$, and its diameter FT' extended passes through 0.

Triangles TET', TDP, and T'FP are all similar and

$\dfrac{TP}{T'P} = \dfrac{2}{1}$. Thus the radius of this smallest circle is $\dfrac{a}{3}$.
Furthermore, arc TP + arc T'P = arc TT'. Accordingly, if
P were to start at X, either circle would generate the
same Deltoid - the circles rolling in opposite direction.
(Notice that PD is the tangent at P.)

2. EQUATIONS: (where a = 3b).

$$\begin{cases} x = b(2\cos t + \cos 2t) \\ y = b(2\sin t - \sin 2t). \end{cases} \quad (x^2+y^2)^2 + 8bx^3 - 24bxy^2 + 18b^2(x^2+y^2) = 27b^4.$$

$$s = \left(\dfrac{8b}{3}\right)\cos 3\varphi. \qquad R^2 + 9s^2 = 64b^2. \qquad r^2 = 9b^2 - 8p^2.$$

$$p = b \cdot \sin 3\varphi. \qquad\qquad z = b(2e^{it} + e^{-2it}).$$

3. METRICAL PROPERTIES:

$$L = 16b. \qquad\qquad \varphi = \pi - \dfrac{t}{2} . \qquad\qquad R = \dfrac{ds}{d\varphi} = -8p.$$

$A = 2\pi b^2$ =   double that of the inscribed circle.

4b = length of tangent (BC) intercepted by the curve.

4. GENERAL ITEMS:

(a) It is the envelope of the Simson line of a fixed
triangle (the line formed by the feet of the perpendiculars dropped onto the sides from a variable point
on the circumcircle). The center of the curve is at
the center of the triangle's nine-point-circle.

(b) Its evolute is another Deltoid.

(c) Kakeya (1) conjectured that it encloses a region
of least area within which a straight rod, taking all
possible orientations in its motion, can be reversed.
However, Besicovitch showed that there is no least
area (2).

(d) Its inverse is a Cotes' Spiral.

(e) Its pedal with respect to (c,0) is the family of
folia

$$[(x - c)^2 + y^2][y^2 + (x - c)x] = 4b(x - c)y^2$$

(reducible to:

$$r = 4b \cos \theta \sin^2\theta - c \cdot \cos \theta)$$

(with respect to a cusp, vertex, or center: a simple, double, tri-folium, resp.).

(f) <u>Tangent Construction</u>: Since T is the instantaneous center of rotation of P, TP is normal to the path. The tangent thus passes through N, the extremity of the diameter through T.

(g) The <u>tangent length</u> intercepted by the curve is constant.

(h) The <u>tangent</u> BC is bisected (at N) by the inscribed circle.

(i) Its <u>catacaustic</u> for a set of parallel rays is an <u>Astroid</u>.

(j) Its <u>orthoptic curve</u> is a <u>Circle</u>. (the inscribed circle).

(k) Its <u>radial curve</u> is a <u>trifolium</u>.

(l) It is the envelope of the tangent fixed at the vertex of a parabola which touches 3 given lines (a Roulette). It is also the envelope of this Parabola.

(m) The tangents at the extremities B, C meet at right angles on the inscribed circle.

(n) The normals to the curve at B, C, and P all meet at T, a point of the circumcircle.

(o) If the tangent BC be held fixed (as a tangent) and the Deltoid allowed to move, the locus of the cusps is a Nephroid. (For an elementary geometrical proof of this elegant property, see Nat. Math. Mag., XIX (1945) p. 330.

74 **DELTOID**

BIBLIOGRAPHY

American Mathematical Monthly, v29, (1922) 160; v46,
   (1939) 85.
Bull. A. M. S., v28 (1922) 45.
Cremona, Crelle (1865).
Ferrers, Quar. Jour. Math. (1866).
L'Interm. d. Math., v3, p.166; v4, 7.
Morley and Morley: Inversive Geometry, G. Bell and Sons
   (1933).
National Mathematics Magazine, XIX (1944-5) 327.
Proc. Edin. Math. Soc., v23, 80.
Serret; Nouv. Ann. (1870).
Townsend, Educ. Times Reprint (1866).
Wieleitner, H.: Spezielle ebene Kurven, Leipsig (1908)
   142
(1) Tohoku Sc. Reports (1917) 71.
(2) Mathematische Zeitschrift (1928) 312.

ENVELOPES

HISTORY: Leibnitz (1694) and Taylor (1715) were the first
to encounter singular solutions of differential equations. Their geometrical significance was first indicated
by Lagrange in 1774. Particular studies were made by
Cayley in 1872 and Hill in 1888 and 1918.

1. DEFINITION: A differential equation of the $\underline{n}$th degree

$$f(x,y,p) = 0, \quad p = \frac{dy}{dx} \,,^*$$

defines $\underline{n}$ p's (real or imaginary)
for every point (x,y) in the plane.
Its solution

$$F(x,y,c) = 0,$$

Fig. 70

of the $\underline{n}$th degree in c, defines
$\underline{n}$ c's for each (x,y). Thus attached to each point in the plane
there are $\underline{n}$ integral curves with
$\underline{n}$ corresponding slopes. Throughout
the plane some of these curves
together with their slopes may be real, some imaginary,
some coincident. The locus of those points where there
are two or more equal values of p, or, which is the same
thing, two or more equal values of c, is the envelope of
the family of its integral curves. In other words, this
envelope is a curve which touches at each of its points
a curve of the family. The equation of the envelope
satisfies the differential equation but is usually not a
member of the family.†

---

* p is used here for the derivative to conform with the general
custom throughout the literature. It should not be confused with
the distance from origin to tangent as used elsewhere in this
book.

† The line y=0 is a part of the envelope and a member of the family $y = c\,(c-4x)^2$

Since a double root of an equation must also be a root of its derivative (and conversely), the envelope is obtained from either of the sets (the discriminant relation):*

$$\begin{cases} f(x,y,p) = 0 \\ f_p(x,y,p) = 0 \end{cases} \qquad \begin{cases} F(x,y,c) = 0 \\ F_c(x,y,c) = 0 \end{cases}$$

Each of these sets constitutes the parametric equations of the envelope.

2. EXAMPLES:

(a) $$\begin{cases} f \equiv y - px - \dfrac{4}{p} = 0 \\ \\ f_p \equiv -x + \dfrac{4}{p^2} = 0. \end{cases}$$

$$\begin{cases} F \cdot \equiv y - cx - \dfrac{4}{c} = 0 \\ \\ F_c \equiv -x + \dfrac{4}{c^2} = 0. \end{cases}$$

yielding: $\boxed{y^2 = 16x}$ as the envelope.

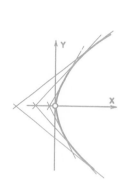

Fig. 71

(b) $$\begin{cases} f \equiv y - px - \dfrac{p}{(p-1)} = 0 \\ \\ f_p \equiv -x + \dfrac{1}{(p-1)^2} = 0. \end{cases}$$

$$\begin{cases} F \equiv x \cdot \sec^2\theta + y \cdot \csc^2\theta - 1 = 0 \\ F_c \equiv 2x \cdot \sec^2\theta \, \tan\theta \\ \qquad\qquad - 2y \cdot \csc^2\theta \, \cot\theta = 0 \, . \end{cases}$$

yielding the parabola $\boxed{\sqrt{x} + \sqrt{y} = +1}$ as the envelope of lines, the sum of whose intercepts is a positive constant.

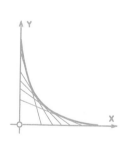

Fig. 72

---

*Such questions as <u>tac locus</u>, <u>cuspidal</u> and <u>nodal loci</u>, etc., whose equations appear as factors in one or both discriminants, are discussed in Hill (1918). For examples, see Cohen, Murray, Glaisher.

NOTE: The two preceeding examples are differential equations of the Clairaut form:

$$y = px + g(p).$$

The method of solution is that of differentiating with respect to x:

$$p = p + x(\frac{dp}{dx}) + (\frac{dg}{dp})(\frac{dp}{dx}).$$

Hence, $(\frac{dp}{dx}) \cdot [x + (\frac{dg}{dp})] = 0$, and the general solution is obtained from the first factor: $\frac{dp}{dx} = 0$, or $p = c$. That is, $y = cx + g(c)$.

The second factor: $x + \frac{dg}{dp} = 0$ is recognized as $f_p = 0$, a requirement for an envelope.

3. TECHNIQUE: A family of curves may be given in terms of two parameters, a, b, which, themselves, are connected by a certain relation. The following method is proper and is particularly adaptable to forms which are homogeneous in the parameters. Thus

given $f(x,y,a,b) = 0$ and $g(a,b) = 0$.

Their partial differentials are

$$f_a da + f_b db = 0 \quad \text{and} \quad g_a da + g_b db = 0$$

and thus $f_a = \lambda g_a$, $f_b = \lambda g_b$,

where λ is a factor of proportionality to be determined. The quantities a, b may be eliminated among the equations to give the envelope. For example:

(a) Consider the envelope of a line of constant length moving with its ends upon the coordinate axes (a Trammel of Archimedes): $\frac{x}{a} + \frac{y}{b} = 1$ where $a^2 + b^2 = 1$. Their differentials give $(\frac{x}{a^2})da + (\frac{y}{b^2})db = 0$ and $a \cdot da + b \cdot db = 0$.

Thus $\frac{x}{a^2} = \lambda a$, $\frac{y}{b^2} = \lambda b$.

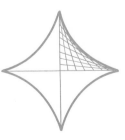

Fig. 73

Multiplying the first by $\underline{a}$, the second by $\underline{b}$, and adding: $\frac{x}{a} + \frac{y}{b} = 1 = \lambda(a^2 + b^2) = \lambda$, by virtue of the given functions. Thus, since $\lambda = 1$ and $a^2 + b^2 = 1$,

$x = a^3$, $y = b^3$, or $\boxed{x^{\frac{2}{3}} + y^{\frac{2}{3}} = 1}$ an Astroid.

(b) Consider concentric and coaxial ellipses of constant area: $\frac{x^2}{a^2} + \frac{y^2}{b^2} = 1$, where

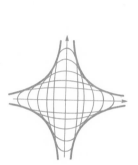

$ab = k$. We have $(\frac{x^2}{a^3})da + (\frac{y^2}{b^3})db = 0$, $b \cdot da + a \cdot db = 0$, from which $\frac{x^2}{a^3} = \lambda b$, $\frac{y^2}{b^3} = \lambda a$. Multiplying the first by $\underline{a}$, the second by $\underline{b}$, and adding:

$1 = 2\lambda ab = 2\lambda k$ and thus $\lambda = \frac{1}{2k}$.

Fig. 74   Thus $\boxed{x^2 y^2 = \frac{k^2}{4}}$, a pair of Hyperbolas.

4. FOLDING THE CONICS: The conics as envelopes of lines may be nicely illustrated by using ordinary wax paper. Let C be the center of a fixed circle of radius $\underline{r}$ and P a fixed point in its plane. Fold P over upon the circle to P' and crease. As P' moves upon the circle, the creases envelope a central conic with P and C as foci:

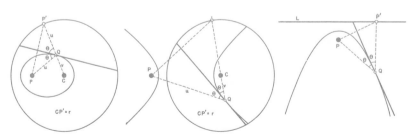

Fig. 75

an Ellipse if P be inside the circle, an Hyperbola if outside. (Draw CP' cutting the crease in Q. Then PQ = P'Q = u, QC = v. For the Ellipse, u + v = r; for the Hyperbola u - v = r. The creases are tangents since they bisect the angles formed by the focal radii.)

For the Parabola, a fixed point P is folded over to P' upon a fixed line L(a circle of infinite radius). P'Q is drawn perpendicular to L and, since PQ = P'Q, the locus of Q is the Parabola with P as focus, L as directrix, and the crease as a tangent. (The simplicity of this demonstration should be compared to an analytical method.) (See Conics 16.)

5. GENERAL ITEMS:

(a) The Evolute of a given curve is the envelope of its normals.

(b) The Catacaustic of a given curve is the envelope of its reflected light rays; the Diacaustic is the envelope of refracted rays.

(c) Curves parallel to a given curve may be considered as:

the envelope of circles of fixed radius with centers on the given curve; or as

the envelope of circles of fixed radius tangent to the given curve; or as

the envelope of lines parallel to the tangent to the given curve and at a constant distance from the tangent.

(d) The first positive Pedal of a given curve is the envelope of circles through the pedal point with the radius vector from the pedal point as diameter.

(e) The first negative Pedal is the envelope of the line through a point of the curve perpendicular to the radius vector from the pedal point.

(f) If L, M, N are linear functions of x,y, the envelope of the family $L \cdot c^2 + 2M \cdot c + N = 0$ is the conic

$$\boxed{M^2 = L \cdot N \quad ,}$$

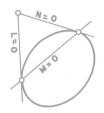

where L = 0, N = 0 are two of its tangents and M = 0 their chord of contact. (Fig. 76).

(g) The envelope of a line (or curve) carried by a curve rolling upon a fixed curve is a <u>Roulette</u>. For example:

the envelope of a diameter of a circle rolling upon a line is a <u>Cycloid</u>;

Fig. 76   the envelope of the directrix of a Parabola rolling upon a line is a <u>Catenary</u>.

(h) An important envelope arises in the following calculus of variations problem (Fig. 77): Given the

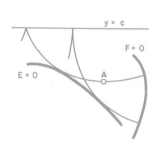

curve F = 0, the point A, both in a plane, and a constant force. Let y = c be the line of zero velocity. The shortest <u>time path</u> from A to F = 0 is the Cycloid normal to F = 0 generated by a circle rolling upon y = c. However, let the family of Cycloids normal to F = 0 generated by all circles rolling upon y = c envelope the curve E = 0. If this envelope passes between A and F = 0, there is no unique solution of the problem.

Fig. 77

BIBLIOGRAPHY

Bliss, G. A.: <u>Calculus of Variations</u>, Open Court (1935).
Cayley, A.: <u>Mess. Math.</u>, II (1872).
Clairaut: <u>Mem. Paris Acad. Sci.</u>, (1734).
Cohen, A.: <u>Differential Equations</u>, D. C. Heath (1933) 86-100.
Glaisher, J. W. L.: <u>Mess. Math.</u>, XII (1882) 1-14 (examples)
Hill, M. J. M.: <u>Proc. Lond. Math. Sc.</u> XIX (1888) 561-589, ibid., S 2, XVII (1918) 149.
Kells, L. M.: <u>Differential Equations</u>, McGraw Hill (1935) 73ff.
Lagrange: <u>Mem. Berlin Acad. Sci.</u>, (1774).
Murray, D. A.: <u>Differential Equations</u>, Longmans, Green (1935) 40-49.

EPI- and HYPO-CYCLOIDS

HISTORY: Cycloidal curves were first conceived by Roemer (a Dane) in 1674 while studying the best form for gear teeth. Galileo and Mersenne had already (1599) discovered the ordinary Cycloid. The beautiful double generation theorem of these curves was first noticed by Daniel Bernoulli in 1725. Astronomers find forms of the cycloidal curves in various coronas (see Proctor). They also occur as Caustics. Rectification was given by Newton in his Principia.

1. DESCRIPTION:

The Epicycloid is generated by a point of a circle rolling externally upon a fixed circle.

The Hypocycloid is generated by a point of a circle rolling internally upon a fixed circle.

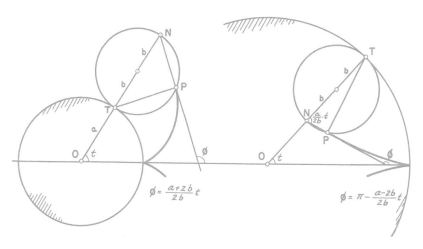

$$\phi = \frac{a+2b}{2b}t$$

$$\phi = \pi - \frac{a-2b}{2b}t$$

Fig. 78

2. DOUBLE GENERATION:

Let the fixed circle have center O and radius OT = OE = a, and the rolling circle center A' and radius

A'T' = A'F = b, the latter carrying the tracing point P.
(See Fig. 79.) Draw ET', OT'F, and PT' to T. Let D be the
intersection of TO and FP and draw the circle on T, P,
and D. This circle is tangent to the fixed circle since
angle DPT is a right angle. Now since PD is parallel to
T'E, triangles OET' and OFD are isosceles and thus

$$DE = 2b.$$

Furthermore,   arc TT' = aθ and   arc T'P = bθ =
arc T'X.

Accordingly,   arc TX = $(a + b)\theta$ = arc TP, for the
Epicycloid,

or   = $(a - b)\theta$ = arc TP, for the
Hypocycloid.

Thus, <u>each of these cycloidal curves may be generated in
two ways: by two rolling circles the sum, or difference,
of whose radii is the radius of the fixed circle.</u>

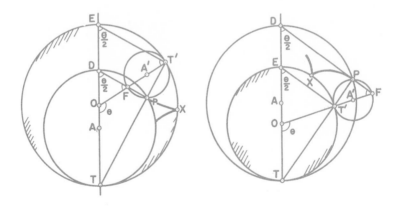

Fig. 79

The theorem is also evident from the analytic viewpoint.
Consider the case of the <u>Hypocycloid</u>: (Euler, 1784)

$$\begin{cases} x = (a - b)\cos t + b \cdot \cos(a - b)\dfrac{t}{b} \\ \\ y = (a - b)\sin t - b \cdot \sin(a - b)\dfrac{t}{b} , \end{cases}$$

and let $b = \dfrac{(a + c)}{2}$, $t = \dfrac{(a + c)t_1}{c}$. The equations become: (dropping subscript)

$$\begin{cases} x = [\dfrac{(a-c)}{2}] \cdot \cos \dfrac{(a+c)t}{c} + \dfrac{(a+c)}{2} \cos \dfrac{(a-c)t}{c} \\ y = [\dfrac{(a-c)}{2}] \cdot \sin \dfrac{(a+c)t}{c} - \dfrac{(a+c)}{2} \sin \dfrac{(a-c)t}{c} . \end{cases}$$

Notice that a change in sign of $\underline{c}$ does not alter these equations. Accordingly, rolling circles of radii $\dfrac{(a + c)}{2}$ or $\dfrac{(a - c)}{2}$ generate the same curve upon a fixed circle of radius $\underline{a}$. That is, the difference of the radii of fixed circle and rolling circle gives the radius of a third circle which will generate the same Hypocycloid.

An analogous demonstration for the Epicycloid can be constructed without difficulty.

3. EQUATIONS:

| EPICYCLOID | HYPOCYCLOID |

$$\begin{cases} x = (a+b)\cos t - b \cdot \cos(a+b)\dfrac{t}{b} \\ y = (a+b)\sin t - b \cdot \sin(a+b)\dfrac{t}{b} . \end{cases} \qquad \begin{cases} x = (a-b)\cos t + b \cdot \cos(a-b)\dfrac{t}{b} \\ y = (a-b)\sin t - b \cdot \sin(a-b)\dfrac{t}{b} . \end{cases}$$

(x-axis through a cusp) (x-axis through a cusp)

$$\begin{cases} x = (a+b)\cos t + b \cdot \cos(a+b)\dfrac{t}{b} \\ y = (a+b)\sin t + b \cdot \sin(a+b)\dfrac{t}{b} \end{cases} \qquad \begin{cases} x = (a-b)\cos t - b \cdot \cos(a-b)\dfrac{t}{b} \\ y = (a-b)\sin t + b \cdot \sin(a-b)\dfrac{t}{b} . \end{cases}$$

(x-axis bisecting arc between 2 successive cusps)

$$s = \dfrac{4b(a + b)}{a} \sin \dfrac{a}{a + 2b} \cdot \varphi , \qquad s = \dfrac{4b(b - a)}{a} \sin \dfrac{a}{a - 2b} \cdot \varphi ,$$

or

$$\boxed{s = A \cdot \sin B\varphi} \; ^* ,$$

where $B < 1$ Epicycloid,

$B = 1$ Ordinary Cycloid,

$B > 1$ Hypocycloid.

*This equation, of course, may just as well involve the cosine.

$$\boxed{R^2 + B^2 s^2 = A^2 B^2}$$

$$\boxed{r^2 = a^2 + \frac{4mp^2}{(m+1)^2}}$$

or $p^2 = C^2(r^2 - a^2)$

where $C^2 = \dfrac{(a + 2b)^2}{4b(a + b)}$

or $= \dfrac{(a - 2b)^2}{4b(b - a)}$,

where $m = \dfrac{(a + b)}{b}$ for the Epicycloid

$m = \dfrac{(b - a)}{b}$ for the Hypocycloid.

$$\boxed{Bp = a \cdot \sin B\varphi}$$

4. METRICAL PROPERTIES:

L (of one arch) $= \dfrac{8b^2 k}{a}$ where $k = \dfrac{(a + b)}{b}$ or $\dfrac{(b - a)}{b}$.

A (of segment formed by one arch and the center)

$= k(k + 1) \cdot \dfrac{\pi a^2}{(k-1)^3}$ where k has the values above.

R = AB·cos $B\varphi = \dfrac{4kp}{(k + 1)^2}$ with the foregoing values of
k. (φ may be obtained in terms of t from the given figures).

[See Am. Math. Monthly (1944) p. 587 for an elementary demonstration of these properties.]

5. SPECIAL CASES:

Epicycloids: If b = a...Cardioid
                  2b = a...Nephroid.

Hypocycloids: If 2b = a...Line Segment (See Trochoids)
                  3b = a...Deltoid
                  4b = a...Astroid.

6. GENERAL ITEMS:

(a) The Evolute of any Cycloidal Curve is another of the same species. (For, since all such curves are of the form: s = A sin Bφ, their evolutes are $\frac{ds}{d\varphi} = \sigma =$ AB sin Bφ. These evolutes are thus Cycloidal Curves similar to their involutes with linear dimensions altered by the factor B. Evolutes of Epicycloids are smaller, those of Hypocycloids larger, than the curves themselves).

(b) The envelope of the family of lines: x cos θ + y sin θ = c·sin(nθ) (with parameter θ) is an Epi- or Hypocycloid.

(c) Pedals with respect to the center are the Rose Curves: r = c·sin(nθ). (See Trochoids).

(d) The isoptic of an Epicycloid is an Epitrochoid (Chasles 1837).

(e) The Epicycloids are Tautochrones (see Ohrtmann).

(f) Tangent Construction: Since T (see figures) is the instantaneous center of rotation of P, TP is normal to the path of P. The perpendicular to TP is thus the tangent at P. The tangent is accordingly the chord of the rolling circle passing through N, the point diametrically opposite T, the point of contact of the circles.

BIBLIOGRAPHY

Edwards, J.: Calculus, Macmillan (1892) 337.
Encyclopaedia Britannica, 14th Ed., "Curves, Special".
Ohrtmann, C.: Das Problem der Tautochronen.
Proctor, R. A.: The Geometry of Cycloids (1878).
Salmon, G.: Higher Plane Curves, Dublin (1879) 278.
Wieleitner, H.: Spezielle ebene Kurven, Leipsig (1908).

EVOLUTES

HISTORY: The idea of evolutes reputedly originated with Huygens in 1673 in connection with his studies on light. However, the concept may be traced to Apollonius (about 200 BC) where it appears in the fifth book of his <u>Conic Sections</u>.

1. DEFINITION: The Evolute of a curve is the locus of its centers of curvature. If (α, β) is this center,

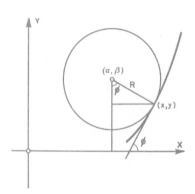

$$\alpha = x - R \cdot \sin \varphi,$$

$$\beta = y + R \cdot \cos \varphi,$$

where R is the radius of curvature, φ the tangential angle, and (x,y) a point of the given curve. The quantities $x, y, R, \sin \varphi, \cos \varphi$ may be expressed in terms of a single variable which acts as a parameter in the equations (in α, β) of the evolute.

Fig. 80

2. IMPORTANT RELATIONS: If s is the arc length of the given curve,

$$\frac{d\alpha}{ds} = \frac{dx}{ds} - R \cos \varphi (d\varphi/ds) - \sin \varphi \left(\frac{dR}{ds}\right),$$

$$\frac{d\beta}{ds} = \frac{dy}{ds} - R \sin \varphi (d\varphi/ds) + \cos \varphi \left(\frac{dR}{ds}\right).$$

But $\quad \sin \varphi = \dfrac{dy}{ds}, \quad \cos \varphi = \dfrac{dx}{ds}, \quad R = \dfrac{ds}{d\varphi}.$

Thus $\quad \dfrac{d\alpha}{ds} = -\sin \varphi \left(\dfrac{dR}{ds}\right), \quad \dfrac{d\beta}{ds} = \cos \varphi \left(\dfrac{dR}{ds}\right).$

Hence $\qquad \boxed{\dfrac{d\beta}{d\alpha} = -\cot \varphi = \dfrac{-1}{y'}.}$

Accordingly, all tangents to the evolute are normals to
the given curve. In other words, <u>the evolute is the
envelope of normals to the given curve</u>.

From the foregoing:

$$d\sigma = \pm\, dR \quad \text{where} \quad d\sigma^2 = d\alpha^2 + d\beta^2.$$

Thus $\boxed{\sigma = R_1 - R_2.}$

That is, <u>the arc length of the
evolute (if R is monotone) is the
difference of the radii of curvature of the given curve measured
from the end points of the arc</u> σ
Furthermore, <u>the given curve is
an involute of its evolute</u>.

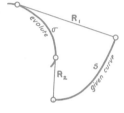

Fig. 81

3. GENERAL ITEMS: [Many of these may be established most
simply by using the Whewell equation of the curve. See
Sec. 7 ff.]

(a) The evolute of a <u>Parabola</u> is a <u>Semi-cubic Para-
bola</u>.

(b) The evolute of a <u>central conic</u> is the <u>Lamé curve</u>:
$$\left(\frac{x}{A}\right)^{\frac{2}{3}} \pm \left(\frac{y}{B}\right)^{\frac{2}{3}} = 1.$$

(c) The evolute of an <u>equiangular spiral</u> is an <u>equal
equiangular spiral</u>.

(d) The evolute of a <u>Tractrix</u> is a <u>Catenary</u>.

(e) Evolutes of the <u>Epi-</u> and <u>Hypocycloids</u> are curves
of the <u>same species</u>. [See Intrinsic Eqns. and 4(b)
following.]

(f) The evolute of a <u>Cayley</u> sextic is a <u>Nephroid</u>.

(g) The Catacaustic of a given curve is the <u>evolute</u> of
its <u>orthotomic curve</u>. (See Caustics.)

(h) Generally, to a flex point on a curve corresponds
an asymptote to its evolute. [For exception see
$y^3 = x^5$, 4(c) following.]

4. EVOLUTES OF SOME CURVES:

  (a) The Conics:

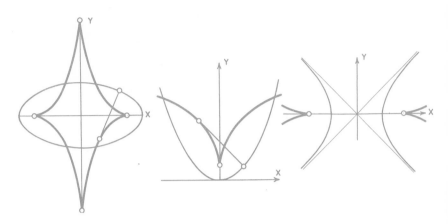

Fig. 82

The Evolute of

  The Ellipse: $(\frac{x}{a})^2 + (\frac{y}{b})^2 = 1$ is $(\frac{x}{A})^{\frac{2}{3}} + (\frac{y}{B})^{\frac{2}{3}} = 1$,

$$Aa = Bb = a^2 - b^2.$$

  The Hyperbola: $(\frac{x}{a})^2 - (\frac{y}{b})^2 = 1$ is $(\frac{x}{H})^{\frac{2}{3}} - (\frac{y}{K})^{\frac{2}{3}} = 1$,

$$Ha = Kb = a^2 + b^2.$$

  The Parabola: $x^2 = 2ky$ is $x^2 = \frac{8}{27k}(y - k)^3$.

(An elegant construction for the center of Curvature of
a conic is given in Conics 20.)

(b) <u>The</u> <u>Cycloids</u> (their evolutes are of the same species):

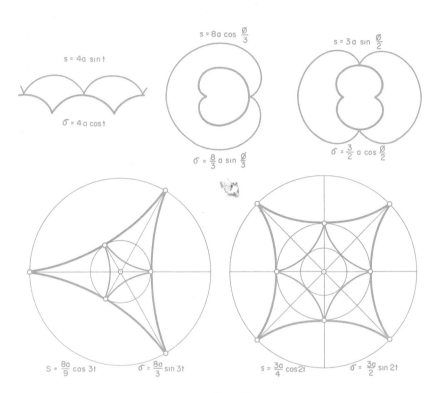

Fig. 83

(c) <u>The</u> <u>Family</u> $y = x^n$.

If the x-axis is tangent at the origin:

$$R_0 = \text{Limit } (\frac{x^2}{2y}) = \text{Limit } (\frac{x^{2-n}}{2}). \quad [\text{See Curvature.}]$$

Thus: $R_0 = 0$ if $n < 2$; $R_0 = \infty$ if $n > 2$;

$$R_0 = \frac{1}{2} \text{ if } n = 2.$$

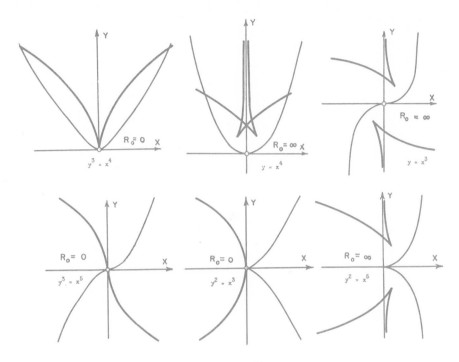

Fig. 84

5. GENERAL NOTE: Where there is symmetry in the given
curve with respect to a line (except for points of
osculation or double flex) there will correspond a <u>cusp</u>
in the evolute (approaching the point of symmetry on
either side, the normal forms a double tangent to the
evolute). This is not sufficient, however.

If a curve has a cusp of the first kind, its evolute in
general passes through the cusp.

If a curve has a cusp of the second kind, there corresponds a <u>flex</u> in the evolute.

6. NORMALS TO A GIVEN CURVE: The Evolute of a curve separates the plane into regions containing points from which normals may be drawn to the curve. For example, consider the Parabola $y^2 = 2x$ and the point (h,k). The normals from (h,k) are determined from

$$y^3 + 2(1 - h)y - 2k = 0,$$

where y represents the ordinates of the feet of the normals at the curve. There are thus, in general, three normals and at their feet:

$$y_1 + y_2 + y_3 = 0.$$

If we ask that two of the three normals be coincident, the foregoing cubic must have a double root. Thus between this cubic and its derivative; $3y^2 + 2(1 - h) = 0$, are the conditions on h and k:

$$h = 1 + \frac{3y^2}{2} , \quad k = -y^3.$$

The locus of (h,k) is thus recognizable as the Evolute of the given Parabola: the envelope of its normals. This evolute divides the plane into two regions from which one or three normals may be drawn to the Parabola. From points on the evolute, two normals may be established.

An elegant theorem is a consequence of the preceding. The circle $x^2 + y^2 + ax + by + c = 0$ meets the Parabola $y^2 = x$ in points such that

$$y_1 + y_2 + y_3 + y_4 = 0.$$

If three of these points are feet of concurrent normals to the Parabola, then $y_4 = 0$ and the circle must necessarily pass through the vertex.

A theorem involving the Cardioid can be obtained here by inversion.

7. INTRINSIC EQUATION OF THE EVOLUTE:

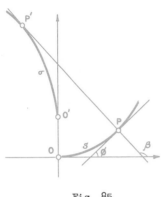

Let the given curve be $s = f(\varphi)$ with the points O' and P' of its evolute corresponding to O and P of the given curve. Then, if σ is the arc length of the evolute:

$$\sigma = R_p - R_o = \frac{ds}{d\varphi} - R_o = f'(\varphi) - R_o.$$

In terms of the tangential angle β, (since $\beta = \varphi + \frac{\pi}{2}$):

$$\sigma = f'(\beta - \frac{\pi}{2}) - R_o$$

Fig. 85

[Example: The Cycloid: $s = 4a \cdot \sin \varphi$; $\sigma = 4a \cdot \cos \varphi = 4a \cdot \cos(\beta - \frac{\pi}{2}) = 4a \cdot \sin \beta$]. (See Cycloid 4,a).

BIBLIOGRAPHY

Byerly, W. E.: Differential Calculus, Ginn and Co. (1879).
Encyclopaedia Britannica, 14th Ed. under "Curves, Special."
Edwards, J.: Calculus, Macmillan (1892) 268 ff.
Salmon, G.: Higher Plane Curves, Dublin (1879) 82 ff.
Wieleitner, H.: Spezielle ebene Kurven, Leipsig (1908) 169 ff.

EXPONENTIAL CURVES

HISTORY: The number "e" can be traced back to Napier and the year 1614 where it entered his system of logarithms. Strangely enough, Napier conceived his idea of logarithms before anything was known of exponents. The notion of a normally distributed variable originated with DeMoivre in 1733 who made known his ideas in a letter to an acquaintance. This was at a time when DeMoivre, banished to England from France, eked out a livelihood by supplying information on games of chance to gamblers. The Bernoulli approach through the binomial expansion was published posthumously in 1713.

1. DESCRIPTION: "e". Fundamental definitions of this important natural constant are:

$$e \equiv \lim_{x \to \infty} \left(1 + \frac{1}{x}\right)^x = \lim_{x \to 0} (1 + x)^{\frac{1}{x}}$$

$$= \sum_0^\infty \frac{1}{k!} \doteq 2.718281 \ .$$

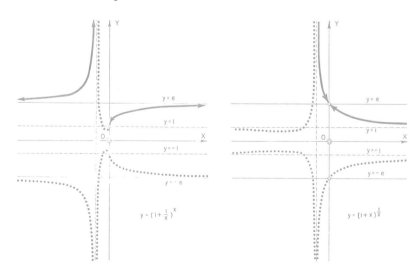

Fig. 86

2. GENERAL ITEMS:

(a) One dollar at 100% interest compounded k times a year produces at the end of the year:

$$S_k = (1 + \frac{1}{k})^k = 1 + 1 + \frac{k(k-1)}{2!} \cdot \frac{1}{k^2} + \frac{k(k-1)(k-2)}{3!} \cdot \frac{1}{k^3} + \ldots + \frac{1}{k^k}$$

dollars.

If the interest be compounded <u>continuously</u>, the total at the end of the year is

$$\underset{k \to \infty}{\text{Limit}} S_k = \underset{k \to \infty}{\text{Limit}} (1 + \frac{1}{k})^k = e \doteq \$2.72.$$

(b) The Euler form:

$$e^{ix} = \cos x + i \cdot \sin x$$

produces the numerical relations:

$$e^{i\pi} + 1 = 0 , \qquad e^{i\frac{\pi}{2}} = i.$$

From the latter

$$(\sqrt{-1})^{\sqrt{-1}} = (e^{i\frac{\pi}{2}})^i = e^{-\frac{\pi}{2}} \doteq 0.208.$$

3. The <u>Law</u> <u>of</u> <u>Growth</u> (or Decay) is the product of experience. In an ideal state (one in which there is no disease, pestilence, war, famine, or the like) many natural populations increase at a rate proportional to the number present. That is, if x represents the number of individuals, and t the time,

$$\frac{dx}{dt} = kx \qquad \text{or} \qquad x = ce^{kt}.$$

This occurs in controlled bacteria cultures, decomposition and conversion of chemical substances (such as radium and sugar), the accumulation of interest bearing money, certain types of electrical circuits, and in the history of colonies such as fruit flies and people.

A further hypothesis supposes the governing law as

$$\frac{dx}{dt} = k \cdot x \cdot (n-x) \qquad \text{or} \qquad x = \frac{cn}{(c + e^{-nkt})}$$

where n is the maximum possible number of inhabitants -
a number regulated, for instance, by the food supply. A
more general form devised to fit observations involves
the function f(t) (which may be periodic, for example):

$$\frac{dx}{dt} = f(t) \cdot x \cdot (n - x) \quad \text{or} \quad x = \frac{cn}{(c + e^{-n \cdot \int f \cdot dt})} \cdot \quad \text{(Fig. 87a)}$$

At moderate velocities, the resistance offered by water
to a ship (or air to an automobile or to a parachute) is
approximately proportional to the velocity. That is,

$$a = \ddot{s} = \dot{v} = -k^2 v, \quad \text{or} \quad s = (\frac{v_0}{k})(1 - e^{-k^2 t}).$$

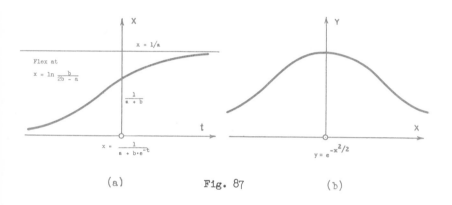

(a)   Fig. 87   (b)

4. THE PROBABILITY (OR NORMAL, OR GAUSSIAN) CURVE:

$$\boxed{y = e^{-x^2/2}.}$$ (Fig. 87b).

(a) Since $y' = -xy$ and $y'' = y(x^2 - 1)$, the flex
points are $(\pm 1, e^{-1/2})$. (An inscribed rectangle with
one side on the x-axis has area $= xy = -y'$. The
largest one is given by $y'' = 0$ and thus two corners
are at the flex points.)

(b) <u>Area</u>. By definition $\Gamma(n) = \int_0^\infty z^{n-1} e^{-z} dz$. In this,

let $\Gamma(n) = \int_0^\infty x^{2n-2} \cdot e^{-x^2} \cdot 2x \; dx = 2 \int_0^\infty x^{2n-1} \cdot e^{-x^2} \cdot dx$.

Putting $n = \frac{1}{2}$,

$$\Gamma(\tfrac{1}{2}) = 2 \int_0^\infty e^{-x^2} dx = \sqrt{\pi} = \text{Area between } y = e^{-x^2} \text{ and}$$

its asymptote.

The <u>Normal</u> <u>Curve</u> is, more specifically:

$$y = \frac{n}{\sigma \cdot \sqrt{2\pi}} \cdot e^{-\frac{(x-\mu)^2}{2\sigma^2}}$$

For this population, n is the size, μ the <u>mean</u>, and σ the <u>standard</u> <u>deviation</u>. Rewriting for simplicity:

$$y = k \cdot e^{-x^2/2\sigma^2},$$

the flex points are $(\pm\sigma, k \cdot e^{-\frac{1}{2}}) = (\pm\sigma, y_0)$. It is evident that the flex tangents:

$$y - y_0 = \mp (\tfrac{y_0}{\sigma})(x \pm \sigma)$$

have <u>x-intercepts</u> <u>which</u> <u>are</u> <u>completely</u> <u>independent</u> <u>of</u> <u>the</u> <u>selected</u> <u>y-unit</u>.

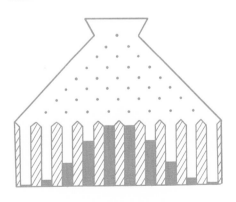

A stream of shot entering the "slot machine" shown is separated by nail obstructions into bins. The collection will form into a histogram approximating the normal curve, the number of shot in the bins proportional to the coefficients in a binomial expansion.

Fig. 88

BIBLIOGRAPHY

Kenney, J. F.: Mathematics of Statistics, Van Nostrand
    II (1941) 7 ff.
Rietz, H. L.: Mathematical Statistics, Open Court (1926).
Steinhaus, H.: Mathematical Snapshots, Stechert (1938)
    120.

FOLIUM OF DESCARTES

HISTORY: First discussed by Descartes in 1638.

1. EQUATIONS:

$$x^3 + y^3 = 3axy$$

(values of t)

$-\infty$ lower -1 upper 0 loop $+\infty$

$$\begin{cases} x = \dfrac{3at}{(1 + t^3)} \\[3mm] y = \dfrac{3at^2}{(1 + t^3)} \end{cases}$$

$$r = \frac{3a \cdot \sin\theta \ \cos\theta}{(\sin^3\theta + \cos^3\theta)}.$$

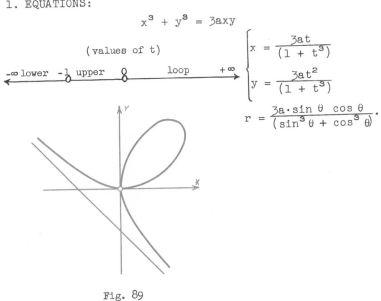

Fig. 89

2. METRICAL PROPERTIES:

(a) Area of loop: $= \dfrac{3a^2}{2}$ = area between curve and asymptote.

3. GENERAL:

    (a) Its asymptote is $x + y + a = 0$.

    (b) Its Hessian is another Folium of Descartes.

BIBLIOGRAPHY

Encyclopaedia Britannica, 14th Ed. under "Curves,
    Special."

FUNCTIONS WITH DISCONTINUOUS PROPERTIES

This collection is composed of illustrations which may be useful at various times as counter examples to the more frequent functions having all the regular properties.

1. FUNCTIONS WITH REMOVABLE DISCONTINUITIES:

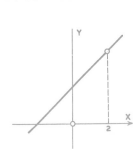

(a) $y = \dfrac{(x^2 - 4)}{(x - 2)}$, undefined for

x = 2, is represented by the line

y = x + 2 except for the point

where x = 2. Since Limit y = 4,
$\qquad\qquad\qquad x \to 2$

this is a removable discontinuity.

Fig. 90

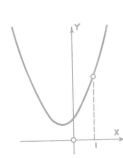

(b) $y = \dfrac{(x^3 - 1)}{(x - 1)}$, undefined for

x = 1, is represented by the Para-

bola $y = x^2 + x + 1$ except for the

point where x = 1. Since Limit y = 3,
$\qquad\qquad\qquad\qquad x \to 1$

this is a removable discontinuity.

Fig. 91

(c) The impor-
tant function
$y = \dfrac{\sin x}{x}$, undefined for
x = 0 has

Limit y = 1
x → 0

and thus has a
removable dis-
continuity. The
hyperbolas
xy = ± 1 form a
bound to the
curve.

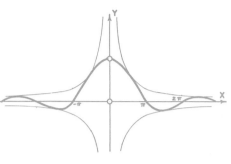

Fig. 92

(d) The function
$y = x \cdot \sin(\dfrac{1}{x})$ is not
defined for x = 0.
However, Limit y = 0
           x → 0
and the function has
a removable disconti-
nuity at x = 0.   The
lines y = ± x form a
bound to the curve
near x = 0.

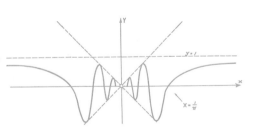

Fig. 93

2. FUNCTIONS WITH NON-REMOVABLE DISCONTINUITIES:

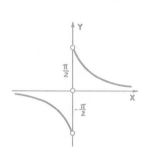

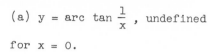

(a) $y = \text{arc tan } \frac{1}{x}$, undefined

for $x = 0$.

$\text{Limit}_{x \to 0+} \; y = \frac{\pi}{2}$; $\text{Limit}_{x \to 0-} \; y = \frac{-\pi}{2}$

The left and right limits are both finite but different.

Fig. 94

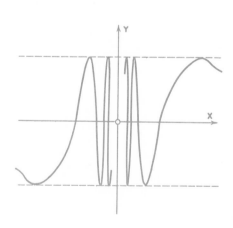

(b) $y = \sin(\frac{1}{x})$ is not defined for $x = 0$. In every neighborhood of $x = 0$, y takes all values between +1 and -1. The x-axis is an asymptote.

$\text{Limit}_{x \to 0} \sin(\frac{1}{x})$ does not exist.

Fig. 95

(c) $y = \text{Limit}\dfrac{(1 + \sin \pi x)^t + 1}{t \to \propto (1 + \sin \pi x)^t - 1}$

is discontinuous for the set:

$\underline{+}\ x = 0, 1, 2, 3, \ldots$

but has values +1 or -1 else-

where.

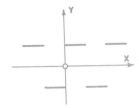

Fig. 96

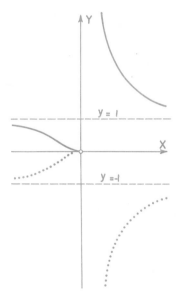

(d) $y = 2^{\frac{1}{x}}$ is undefined for

$x = 0$. Limit $y = 0$;
      $x \to 0-$

Limit $y = \infty$ Left and right
$x \to 0+$

limits different.

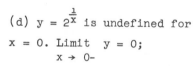

Fig. 97

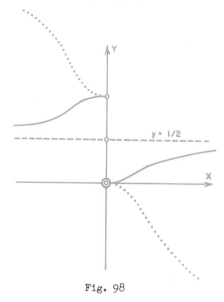

(e) $y = \dfrac{1}{2^{\frac{1}{x}} + 1}$

is undefined for $x = 0$.

Since $\underset{x \to 0-}{\text{Limit}}\ y = 1$, and

$\underset{x \to 0+}{\text{Limit}}\ y = 0$, left and

right limits at $x = 0$
are both finite but
different.

Fig. 98

3. OTHER TYPES OF DISCONTINUITIES:

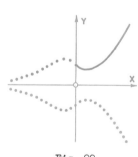

(a) $y = x^x$ is undefined for

$x = 0$, but $\underset{x \to 0+}{\text{Limit}}\ y = 1$.

The function is <u>everywhere</u> dis-
<u>continuous</u> for $x < 0$.

Fig. 99

(b) $y = x^{\frac{1}{x}}$ is undefined for x = 0, but Limit y = 0.
$$x \to 0+$$
The function is everywhere discontinuous for x < 0.

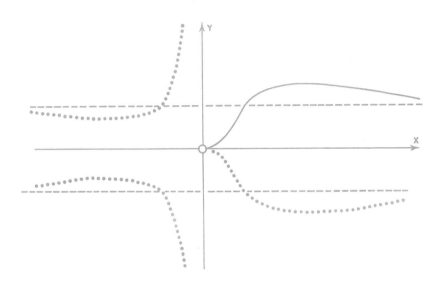

Fig. 100

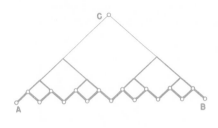

Fig. 101

(c) By halving the sides AC and CB of the isosceles triangle ABC, and continuing this process as shown, the "saw tooth" path between A and B is produced. This path is continuous with constant length. The nth successive curve of this procession has no unique slope at the set of points whose coordinates, measured from A, are of the form

$$K \cdot \frac{AB}{2^n} , \quad K = 1, \ldots, n.$$

(d) The "snowflake" (Von Koch curve) is the limit of the procession shown.[*] (Each side of the original

Fig. 102

equilateral triangle is trisected, the middle segment discarded and an external equilateral triangle built there). The limiting curve has <u>finite area</u>, <u>infinite length</u>, and <u>no derivative anywhere</u>.

The determination of length and area are good exercises in numerical series.

---

[*] This procession is the one devised by Boltzmann to visualize certain theorems in the theory of gases. See Math. Annalen, 50(1898).

(e) The Sierpinski "space-filling" curve is the limit of the procession shown. It has <u>finite</u> <u>area</u>, <u>infinite</u>

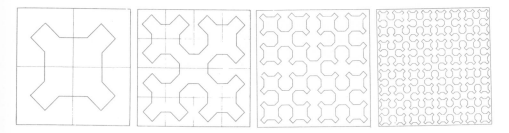

Fig. 103

<u>length</u>, <u>no derivative anywhere</u>, and <u>passes through every point within the original square</u>.

(f) The Weierstrass function $y = \sum\limits_{0}^{\infty} b^n \cdot \cos(a^n \pi x)$,

where <u>a</u> is an odd positive integer, <u>b</u> a positive constant less than unity, although continuous has <u>no derivative anywhere</u> if

$$ab > 1 + \frac{3\pi}{2}$$

BIBLIOGRAPHY

Edwards, J.: <u>Calculus</u>, Macmillan (1892) 235.
Hardy, G. H.: <u>Pure Mathematics</u>, Macmillan (1933) 162 ff.
Kasner and Newman: <u>Mathematics and Imagination</u>, Simon and Schuster (1940).
Osgood, W. F.: <u>Real Variables</u>, Stechert (1938) Chap. III.
Pierpont, J.: <u>Real Variables</u>, Ginn and Co. (1912) Chap. XIV.
Steinhaus, H.: <u>Mathematical Snapshots</u>, Stechert (1938) 60.

GLISSETTES

HISTORY: The idea of Glissettes in somewhat elementary
form was known to the ancient Greeks. (For example, the
Trammel of Archimedes, the Conchoid of Nicomedes.) A
systematic study, however, was not made until 1869 when
Besant published a short tract on the matter.

1. DEFINITION: A Glissette is the locus of a point - or
the envelope of a curve - carried by a curve which slides
between given curves.

   An interesting and related Glissette is that generated
by a curve always tangent at a fixed point of a given
curve. (See 6b and 6c below.)

2. SOME EXAMPLES:

   (a) The Glissette of the vertex P of a rigid angle
   whose sides slide upon two fixed points A and B is an
   arc of a circle. Furthermore, since P travels on a
   circle, any point Q of AP describes a Limacon.
   (See 4).

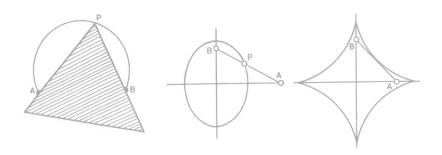

Fig. 104

   (b) Trammel of Archimedes.

   A rod AB of fixed length slides with its ends
   upon two fixed perpendicular lines.

1. The Glissette of any point P of the rod (or any point rigidly attached) is an Ellipse.

2. The envelope Glissette of the rod itself is the Astroid. (See Envelopes, 3a.)

(c) If a point A of a rod, which passes always through a fixed point O, moves along a given curve $r = f(\theta)$, the Glissette of a point P of the rod k units distant from A is the Conchoid

$$r = f(\theta) + k$$

of the given curve. [See Moritz, R. E., U. of Wash. Pub. 1923, for pictures of many varieties of this family,

Fig. 105

where the base curve is $r = \cos(\dfrac{p\theta}{q})$].

3. THE POINT GLISSETTE OF A CURVE SLIDING BETWEEN TWO LINES AT RIGHT ANGLES (THE x,y AXES):

If the curve be given by $p = f(\varphi)$ referred to the carried point P, then

$$y = p = f(\varphi) \text{ and } x = f(\varphi + \frac{\pi}{2})$$

are parametric equations of the Glissette traced by P.

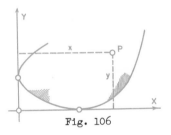

Fig. 106

For example, the Astroid $p = \sin 2\varphi$, referred to its center, has the Glissette

$$x = \sin 2\varphi, \quad y = -\sin 2\varphi$$

(a segment of $x + y = 0$) as the locus of its center as it slides between the x and y axes.

4. A TRIANGLE TOUCHING TWO FIXED CIRCLES:

Consider the envelope of a side BC of a given triangle ABC, two of whose sides touch fixed circles with

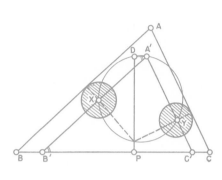

centers X, Y. As this
triangle moves, lines
XA' and YA' drawn
parallel to the sides
are lines fixed to the
triangle. Let the circle
described by A' meet the
parallel to BC through
A' in D. Then angle
DA'X = angle A'B'C =
angle ABC, all con-
stant, and thus D is a
fixed point of the
circle. The perpendicu-
lar DP from D to BC is
the altitude of the in-

Fig. 107

variable triangle A'B'C' and thus BC touches the circle
with that altitude as radius and center D.*

The point Glissettes (for example, any point F of
A'C') of the triangle are Limacons. (See Trochoids 3d.)

5. GENERAL THEOREM: <u>Any</u> <u>motion</u> <u>of</u> <u>a</u> <u>configuration</u> <u>in</u> <u>its</u>
<u>plane</u> <u>can</u> <u>be</u> <u>represented</u> <u>by</u> <u>the</u> <u>rolling</u> <u>of</u> <u>a</u> <u>certain</u>
<u>determinate</u> <u>curve</u> <u>on</u> <u>another</u> <u>determinate</u> <u>curve</u>. This

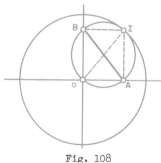

reduces the problem of Glissettes to that of Roulettes.
A simple illustration is the
trammel AB sliding upon two
perpendicular lines. I, the
instantaneous center of rotation of AB, lies always on
the fixed circle with center
O and radius AB. This point
also lies on the circle having
AB as diameter - a circle carried with AB. The action then

Fig. 108

*Thus the sides of any polygon envelope circles if two sides
touch circles or pass through two fixed points. This enters the
design of a rotor, a convex curve which remains tangent to all
sides of a fixed polygon while the curve is rotated. See
Goldberg, M.: A.M.M. v55, 393-402.

is as if this smaller circle were rolling internally upon a fixed circle twice as large. Hence, any point of AB describes an Ellipse and the envelope of AB is the Astroid.

6. GENERAL ITEMS:

(a) A Parabola slides on the x,y axes. The locus of the vertex is:

$$x^2y^2(x^2 + y^2 + 3a^2) = a^6 \; ;$$

the focus is:

$$x^2y^2 = a^2(x^2 + y^2).$$

(b) The path of the center of an Ellipse touching a straight line always at the same point is

$$x^2y^2 = (a^2 - y^2)(y^2 - b^2).$$

(c) A Parabola slides on a straight line touching it at a fixed point of the line. The locus of the focus is an Hyperbola.

(d) The bar APB, with PA = a, PB = b, moves with its ends on a simple closed curve. The difference between the area of the curve and the area of the locus described by P is πab.

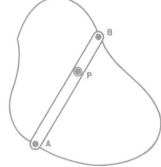

Fig. 109

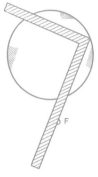

(e) The vertex of a carpenter's square moves upon a circle while one arm passes through a fixed point F. The <u>envelope</u> of the other arm is a conic with F as focus. (Hyperbola if F is outside the circle. Ellipse if inside, Parabola if the circle be replaced by a line.) (See Conics 16.)

Fig. 110

BIBLIOGRAPHY

<u>American</u> <u>Mathematical</u> <u>Monthly</u>: v 52, 384 ; v 55, 393-402.
Besant, W. H.: <u>Roulettes</u> <u>and</u> <u>Glissettes</u>, London (1870).
<u>Encyclopaedia</u> <u>Britannica</u>, 14th Ed., "Curves, Special."
Walker, G.: <u>National</u> <u>Mathematics</u> <u>Magazine</u>, 12,13 (1937-8, 1938-9).

HYPERBOLIC FUNCTIONS

HISTORY: Of disputed origin: either by Mayer or by Riccati in the 18th century; elaborated upon by Lambert (who proved the irrationality of π). Further investigated by Gudermann (1798-1851), a teacher of Weierstrass. He complied 7-place tables for logarithms of the hyperbolic functions in 1832.

1. DESCRIPTION: These functions are defined as follows:

$$\sinh x = \frac{(e^x - e^{-x})}{2} \ , \ \cosh x = \frac{(e^x + e^{-x})}{2} = \sqrt{(1 + \sinh^2 x)},$$

$$\tanh x = \frac{\sinh x}{\cosh x} \ , \ \coth x = \frac{1}{\tanh x} \ ,$$

$$\operatorname{sech} x = \frac{1}{\cosh x} \ , \ \operatorname{csch} x = \frac{1}{\sinh x} \ .$$

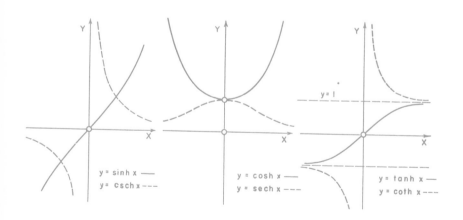

y = sinh x ——
y = csch x ---

y = cosh x ——
y = sech x ---

y = tanh x ——
y = coth x ---

Fig. 111

2. INTERRELATIONS:

    (a) <u>Inverse Relations</u>:

$$\text{arc sinh } x = \ln(x + \sqrt{x^2 + 1}), \ x^2 < \infty;$$

$$\text{arc cosh } x = \ln(x \pm \sqrt{x^2 - 1}), \ x > 1;$$

$$\text{arc tanh } x = (\tfrac{1}{2})\ln\left[\frac{(1+x)}{(1-x)}\right], \ x^2 < 1;$$

$$\text{arc coth } x = (\tfrac{1}{2})\ln\left[\frac{(x+1)}{(x-1)}\right], \ x^2 > 1;$$

$$\text{arc sech } x = \ln\left(\frac{1}{x} + \sqrt{\frac{1}{x^2} - 1}\right), \ 0 < x^2 \le 1;$$

$$\text{arc csch } x = \ln\left(\frac{1}{x} + \sqrt{\frac{1}{x^2} + 1}\right), \ x^2 > 0.$$

    (b) <u>Identities</u>:

$$\cosh^2 x - \sinh^2 x = 1; \ \text{sech}^2 x = 1 - \tanh^2 x;$$

$$\text{csch}^2 x = \coth^2 x - 1;$$

$$\sinh(x \pm y) = \sinh x \cdot \cosh y \pm \cosh x \cdot \sinh y;$$

$$\cosh(x \pm y) = \cosh x \cdot \cosh y \pm \sinh x \cdot \sinh y;$$

$$\sinh 2x = 2\sinh x \cdot \cosh x;$$

$$\cosh 2x = \cosh^2 x + \sin^2 x;$$

$$\tan(x \pm y) = \frac{\tanh x \pm \tanh y}{1 \pm \tanh x \tanh y} \ ; \ \sinh \frac{x}{2} = \pm\sqrt{\frac{\cosh x - 1}{2}};$$

$$\cosh \frac{x}{2} = \pm\sqrt{\frac{\cosh x + 1}{2}} \ ;$$

$$\sinh x + \sinh y = 2\sinh \frac{x+y}{2} \cosh \frac{x-y}{2} \ ;$$

$$\cosh x + \cosh y = 2\cosh \frac{x+y}{2} \cosh \frac{x-y}{2} \ ;$$

$$\sinh 3x = 4\sinh^3 x + 3\sinh x;$$

$$\cosh 3x = 4\cosh^3 x - 3\cosh x;$$

$$(\sinh x + \cosh x)^k = \sinh kx + \cosh kx.$$

(c) <u>Differentials</u> <u>and</u> <u>Integrals</u>:

$d(\sinh x) = \cosh x \cdot dx;$ $\int \tanh x\, dx = \ln \cosh x;$

$d(\cosh x) = \sinh x\, dx;$ $\int \coth x\, dx = \ln |\sinh x| :$

$d(\tanh x) = \operatorname{sech}^2 x\, dx;$ $\int \operatorname{sech} x\, dx = \arctan(\sinh x) = \operatorname{gd} x^* ;$

$d(\coth x) = -\operatorname{csch}^2 x\, dx;$ $\int \operatorname{csch} x\, dx = \ln|\tanh(\frac{x}{2})| ;$

$d(\operatorname{sech} x) = -\operatorname{sech} x \cdot \tanh x\, dx;$

$d(\operatorname{csch} x) = -\operatorname{csch} x \cdot \coth x\, dx;$

$d(\operatorname{arc\,sinh} x) = \pm \dfrac{dx}{\sqrt{x^2 + 1}} ;$ $d(\operatorname{arc\,cosh} x) = {\textstyle\pm} \dfrac{dx}{\sqrt{x^2 - 1}} ;$

$d(\operatorname{arc\,tanh} x) = \dfrac{dx}{(1 - x^2)} = d(\operatorname{arc\,coth} x),$ (in different intervals);

$d(\operatorname{arc\,sech} x) = {\textstyle\pm} \dfrac{dx}{x\sqrt{1 - x^2}};$ $d(\operatorname{arc\,csch} x) = \dfrac{\pm dx}{x\sqrt{1 + x^2}}$

---

* (called the "gudermannian") $\quad x = \displaystyle\int_0^y \sec y\, dy = \ln|\sec y + \tan y| .$

3. ATTACHMENT TO THE RECTANGULAR HYPERBOLA: A comparison with the trigonometric (circular) functions is as follows.

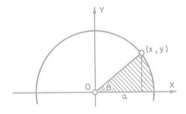
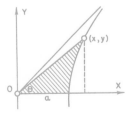

Fig. 112

For the shaded sectors (A):

$$\begin{cases} x = a \cdot \cos t \\ y = a \cdot \sin t \ . \end{cases} \qquad\qquad \begin{cases} x = a \cdot \cosh t \\ y = a \cdot \sinh t \ . \end{cases}$$

$$dA = (\frac{1}{2})\rho^2 d\theta,$$

$$\theta = \text{arc tan} \ \frac{y}{x} = t, \qquad\qquad \theta = \text{arc tan} \ \frac{y}{x} = \text{arc tan}(\tanh t),$$

$$d\theta = dt. \qquad\qquad d\theta = \frac{dt}{(\cosh^2 t + \sinh^2 t)}$$

But

$$\rho^2 = a^2(\cos^2 t + \sin^2 t) = a^2, \qquad\qquad \rho^2 = a^2(\cosh^2 t + \sinh^2 t),$$

and thus

$$A = (\frac{1}{2}) \int_0^t a^2 dt = \frac{a^2 t}{2} \ . \qquad\qquad A = (\frac{1}{2}) \int_0^t a^2 dt = \frac{a^2 t}{2} \ .$$

In either case:

$$t = \frac{2A}{a^2} \ ,$$

or

$$\begin{cases} x = a \cdot \cos \dfrac{2A}{a^2} \\[2mm] y = a \cdot \sin \dfrac{2A}{a^2} \ . \end{cases} \qquad\qquad \begin{cases} x = a \cdot \cosh \dfrac{2A}{a^2} \\[2mm] y = a \cdot \sinh \dfrac{2A}{a^2} \ . \end{cases}$$

Thus the Hyperbolic functions are attached to the Rectangular Hyperbola in the same manner that the trigonometric functions are attached to the circle.

4. ANALYTICAL RELATIONS WITH THE TRIGONOMETRIC FUNCTIONS:

The Euler forms:

$$e^{ix} = \cos x + i \cdot \sin x; \quad e^{-x} = \cos(ix) + i \cdot \sin(ix);$$

$$e^{-ix} = \cos x - i \cdot \sin x; \quad e^{x} = \cos(ix) - i \cdot \sin(ix);$$

produce:

$$\cosh(ix) = \cos x; \qquad \cosh x = \cos(ix);$$

$$\sinh(ix) = i \cdot \sin x; \qquad \sinh x = -i \cdot \sin(ix);$$

from which other relations may be derived.

5. SERIES REPRESENTATIONS:

$$\sinh x = \sum_{1}^{\infty} \frac{x^{2k-1}}{(2k-1)!} \ , \qquad x^2 < \infty ;$$

$$\cosh x = \sum_{0}^{\infty} \frac{x^{2k}}{(2k)!} \ , \qquad x^2 < \infty ;$$

$$\tanh x = x - \frac{x^3}{3} + \frac{2x^5}{15} + \frac{17x^7}{315} + \ldots, \quad x^2 < \frac{\pi^2}{4} \ ;$$

$$\coth x = \frac{1}{x} + \frac{x}{3} - \frac{x^3}{45} + \frac{2x^5}{945} - \frac{x^7}{4725} + \ldots, \quad x^2 < \pi^2 \ ;$$

$$\text{sech } x = 1 - \frac{1}{2} x^2 + \frac{5}{4!} x^4 - \frac{61}{6!} x^6 + \frac{1385}{8!} x^8 - \ldots, \quad x^2 < \frac{\pi^2}{4} \ ;$$

$$\text{csch } x = \frac{1}{x} - \frac{x}{6} + \frac{7x^3}{360} - \frac{31x^5}{15120} + \ldots, \quad x^2 < \pi^2 \ ;$$

$$\text{arc sinh } x = x - \frac{1}{2} \cdot \frac{x^3}{3} + \frac{1\cdot3}{2\cdot4} \frac{x^5}{5} - \frac{1\cdot3\cdot5}{2\cdot4\cdot6} \frac{x^7}{7} + \ldots, \quad x \leq 1 \ ,$$

$$= \ln 2x + \frac{1}{2} \cdot \frac{1}{2x^2} - \frac{1\cdot3}{2\cdot4} \frac{1}{4x^4} + \frac{1\cdot3\cdot5}{2\cdot4\cdot6} \frac{1}{6x^6} + \ldots, \quad x \geq 1 \ ;$$

$$\text{arc cosh } x = \ln 2x - \frac{1}{2} \frac{1}{2x^2} - \frac{1\cdot3}{2\cdot4} \frac{1}{4x^4} - \frac{1\cdot3\cdot5}{2\cdot4\cdot6} \frac{1}{6x^6} + \ldots, \quad x \geq 1 \ ;$$

$$\text{arc tanh } x = \sum_{1}^{\infty} \frac{x^{2k-1}}{2k - 1} \ ;$$

$$\text{gd } x = \text{arc tan (sinh } x) = x - \frac{1}{6} x^3 + \frac{1}{24} x^5 - \frac{61}{5040} x^7 + \ldots.$$

6. APPLICATIONS:

(a) $y = a \cdot \cosh \frac{x}{a}$, the Catenary, is the form of a flexible chain hanging from two supports.

(b) These functions play a dominant role in electrical communication circuits. For example, the engineer prefers the convenient hyperbolic form over the exponential form of the solutions of certain types of problems in transmission. The voltage V (or current I) satisfies the differential equation

$$\frac{d^2V}{dx^2} = zy \cdot V,$$

where x is distance along the line, y the unit shunt
admittance, and z the series impedance. The solution:

$$V = V_r \cdot \cosh x \sqrt{yz} \; + \; I_r \cdot \sqrt{\frac{z}{y}} \cdot \sinh x \sqrt{yz} \; ,$$

gives the voltage in terms of voltage and current at
the receiving end.

(c) Mapping: In the general problem of conformal
world maps, hyperbolic functions enter significantly.
For instance, in Mercator's (1512-1594) projection
of the sphere onto its tangent cylinder with the N-S
line as axis,

$$x = \theta, \quad \varphi = gd \; y,$$

where (x,y) is the projection of the point on the
sphere whose latitude and longitude are φ and θ, respectively. Along a <u>rhumb</u> <u>line</u>,

$$\varphi = gd(\theta \cdot \tan \alpha + b),$$

where α is the inclination of a straight course (line)
on the map.

BIBLIOGRAPHY

Kennelly, A. E.: <u>Applic.</u> <u>of</u> <u>Hyp.</u> <u>Functions</u> <u>to</u> <u>Elec.</u> <u>Engr.</u>
    <u>Problems</u>, McGraw-Hill (1912).
Merriman and Woodward: <u>Higher</u> <u>Mathematics</u>, John Wiley
    (1896) 107 ff.
Slater, J. C.: <u>Microwave</u> <u>Transmission,</u> McGraw-Hill (1942)
    8 ff.
Ware and Reed: <u>Communication</u> <u>Circuits</u>, John Wiley (1942)
    52 ff.

INSTANTANEOUS CENTER OF ROTATION and
THE CONSTRUCTION OF SOME TANGENTS

1. DEFINITION: A rigid body moving in any manner whatso-
ever in a plane has an instanta-
neous center of rotation. This
center may be located if the
direction of motion of any two
points A, B of the body are known.
Let their respective velocities be
V_1 and V_2. Draw the perpendiculars
to V_1 and V_2 at A and B. The center of rotation is their point of
intersection H. For, no point of
HA can move toward A or H (since
the body is rigid) and thus all
points must move parallel to V_1.
Similarly, all points of HB move
parallel to V_2. But the point H cannot move parallel to
both V_1 and V_2 and so must be at rest.

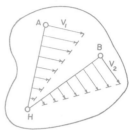

Fig. 113

2. CENTRODE: If two points of a rigid body move on known
curves, the instantaneous center
of rotation of any point P of the
body is H, the intersection of
the normals to the two curves.
The locus of the point H is
called the Centrode. (Chasles)

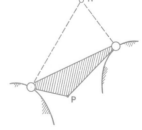

Fig. 114

3. EXAMPLES:

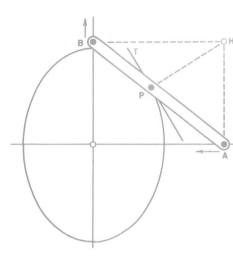

Fig. 115

(a) The Ellipse is produced by the Trammel of Archimedes. The extremities A, B of a rod move along two perpendicular lines. The path of any point P of the rod is an Ellipse.* AH and BH are normals to the directions of A and B and thus H is the center of rotation of any point of the rod. HP is normal to the path of P and its perpendicular PT is the tangent. (See Trochoids, 3c.)

(b) The Conchoid [†] is the path of P_1 and P_2 where A, the midpoint of the constant distance P_1P_2, moves along the fixed line and P_1P_2 (extended) passes through the fixed point O. The point of P_1P_2 passing through O has the direction of P_1P_2. Thus the perpendiculars OH and AH locate H the center of rotation. The perpendiculars to

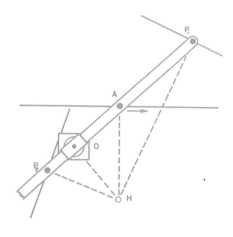

Fig. 116

---

* The path of P is an Ellipse if A and B move along any two intersecting lines.

[†] (For a more general definition, see Conchoid, 1.)

P_1H and P_2H at P_1 and P_2 respectively, are tangents to the curve.

(c) For the <u>Limacon</u>, B moves along the circle while OBP rotates about O. At any instant B moves normal to the radius BA while the point on OP at O moves in the direction OP. The center of rotation is thus H (a point of the circle) and the tangent to the Limacon described by P is perpendicular to PH.

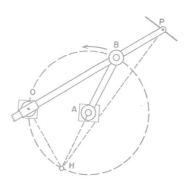

Fig. 117

(d) The <u>Isoptic</u> of a curve is the locus of the inter-section of two tangents which meet at a constant angle. If these tangents meet the curve in A and B, the normals there to the given curve meet in H. This is the center of rotation of any point of the rigid body formed by the constant angle. Thus HP is normal to the path of P. For example, (see Glissettes, 4) the locus of the vertex of a triangle, two of whose sides touch fixed circles, is a Limacon. Normals to these tangents pass through the centers of the circles and make a con-stant angle with each other. They meet at H, the center of rotation, and the locus of H is accordingly a circle through the centers of the two given circles.

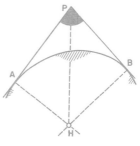

Fig. 118

(e) The point <u>Glissette</u> of a curve is the locus of P, a point rigidly attached to the curve, as that curve slides on given fixed curves. If the points of tangency are A and B, the normals to the fixed curves there meet in H, the center of rotation. Thus HP is normal to the path of P.

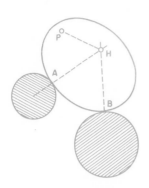

Fig. 119

(f) <u>Trochoidal</u> curves are generated by a point P rigidly attached to a curve that rolls upon a fixed curve. The point of tangency H is the center of rotation and HP is normal to the path of P. This is particularly useful in the trochoids of a circle: the Epi- and Hypocycloids and the ordinary Cycloid.

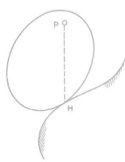

Fig. 120

BIBLIOGRAPHY

Chasles, M.: <u>Histoire</u> <u>de</u> <u>la</u> <u>Géométrie</u>, Bruxelles (1881) 548.
Keown and Faires: <u>Mechanism</u>, McGraw-Hill (1931) Chap. V.
Niewenglowski, B.: <u>Cours</u> <u>de</u> <u>Géométrie</u> <u>Analytique</u>, I (Paris) (1894) 347 ff.
Williamson, B.: <u>Calculus</u>, Longmans, Green (1895) 359.

INTRINSIC EQUATIONS

INTRODUCTION: The choice of reference system for a particular curve may be dictated by its physical characteristics or by the particular type of information desired from its properties. Thus, a system of <u>rectangular</u> <u>coordinates</u> will be selected for curves in which <u>slope</u> is of primary importance. Curves which exhibit a <u>central</u> <u>property</u> - physical or geometrical - with respect to a point will be expressed in a polar system with the central point as pole. This is well illustrated in situations involving action under a central force: the path of the earth about the sun for example. Again, if an outstanding feature is the distance from a fixed point upon the tangent to a curve - as in the general problem of Caustics - a system of <u>pedal</u> <u>coordinates</u> will be selected.

The equations of curves in each of these systems, however, are for the most part "local" in character and are altered by certain transformations. Let a transformation (within a particular system or from system to system) be such that the measures of length and angle are preserved. Then <u>area</u>, <u>arc</u> <u>length</u>, <u>curvature</u>, <u>number</u> <u>of</u> <u>singular</u> <u>points</u>, etc., will be invariants. If a curve can be properly defined in terms of these invariants its equation would be intrinsic in character and would express qualities of the curve which would not change from system to system.

Two such characterizations are given here. One, relating arc length and tangential angle, was introduced by Whewell; the other, connecting arc length and curvature, by Cesáro.

1. THE WHEWELL EQUATION: The Whewell equation is that connecting arc length s and tangential angle φ, where φ is measured from the tangent to the curve at the initial point of the arc. It will be convenient here to take this tangent as the x-axis or, in polar coordinates, the initial line. Examples follow.

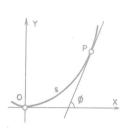

Fig. 121

(a) Consider the Catenary: $y = a \cdot \cosh(\frac{x}{a})$.

Here $y' = \sinh(\frac{x}{a}) = \tan \varphi$; $ds^2 = [1 + \sinh^2(\frac{x}{a})]dx^2$.

Thus $s = \int_0^x \cosh(\frac{x}{a})dx = a \cdot \sinh(\frac{x}{a})$, and $\boxed{s = a \cdot \tan \varphi}$

(This relation is, of course, a direct consequence of the physical definition of the curve.)

(b) Consider the Cardioid: $r = 2a(1 - \cos \theta)$.

Here $\tan \psi = \frac{(1 - \cos \theta)}{\sin \theta} = \tan(\frac{\theta}{2})$ and thus $\psi = \frac{\theta}{2}$.

However, $\varphi = \psi + \theta$, and thus $\varphi = \frac{3\theta}{2}$

The arc length: $ds^2 = 8a^2(1 - \cos \theta)d\theta^2$

$$s = -8a \cdot \cos(\frac{\theta}{2}) = \boxed{-8a \cdot \cos(\frac{\varphi}{3})}$$

The equation of an <u>involute</u> <u>of</u> <u>a</u> <u>given</u> <u>curve</u> is obtained directly from the Whewell equation by integration. For example,

the <u>circle</u>: $\sigma = a \cdot \varphi$

has for an <u>involute</u>: $s = \dfrac{a\varphi^2}{2}$,

the constant of integration determined conveniently.

NOTE: The inclination φ depends of course upon the tangent to the curve at the selected point from which <u>s</u> is measured. If this point were selected where the tangent is perpendicular to the original choice, the Whewell equation would involve the co-function of φ. Thus, for example, the Cardioid may be given by either of the equations: $s = k \cdot \cos\left(\dfrac{\varphi}{3}\right)$ or $s = k \cdot \sin\left(\dfrac{\varphi}{3}\right)$.

2. THE CESARO EQUATION: The Cesáro equation relates arc length and radius of curvature. Such equations are definitive and follow directly from the Whewell equations. For example, consider the general family of Cycloidal curves:

$$s = a \cdot \sin b\varphi.$$

Here
$$R = \frac{ds}{d\varphi} = ab \cdot \cos b\,\varphi.$$

Accordingly, $R^2 + b^2 \cdot s^2 = a^2 b^2.$

INTRINSIC EQUATIONS

3. INTRINSIC EQUATIONS OF SOME CURVES:

Curve	Whewell Equation	Ceśaro Equation
Astroid	$s = a \cdot \cos 2\varphi$	$4s^2 + R^2 = 4a^2$
Cardioid	$s = a \cdot \cos\left(\frac{\varphi}{3}\right)$	$s^2 + 9R^2 = a^2$
Catenary	$s = a \cdot \tan \varphi$	$s^2 + a^2 = aR$
Circle	$s = a \cdot \varphi$	$R = a$
Cissoid	$s = a(\sec^3\varphi - 1)$	$729(s+a)^8 = a^2[9(s+a)^2 + R^2]^3$
Cycloid	$s = a \cdot \sin \varphi$	$s^2 + R^2 = a^2$
Deltoid	$s = \dfrac{8b}{3} \cos 3\varphi$	$9s^2 + R^2 = 64b^2$
Epi- and Hypo-cycloids	$s = a \cdot \sin b\varphi$ *	$R^2 + b^2 \cdot s^2 = a^2 b^2$
Equiangular Spiral	$s = a \cdot (e^{m\varphi} - 1)$	$m(s + a) = R$
Involute of Circle	$s = \dfrac{a \cdot \varphi^2}{2}$	$2a \cdot s = R^2$
Nephroid	$s = 6b \cdot \sin \dfrac{\varphi}{2}$	$4R^2 + s^2 = 36b^2$
Tractrix	$s = a \cdot \ln \sec \varphi$	$a^2 + R^2 = a^2 \cdot e^{2s/a}$

     * $b < 1$ Epi.

        $b = 1$ Ordinary.

        $b > 1$ Hypo.

BIBLIOGRAPHY

Boole, G.: Differential Equations, London, 263.
Cambridge Philosophical Transactions: VIII 689; IX 150.
Edwards, J.: Calculus, Macmillan (1892).

INVERSION

HISTORY: Geometrical inversion seems to be due to
Steiner ("the greatest geometer since Apollonius") who
indicated a knowledge of the subject in 1824. He was
closely followed by Quetelet (1825) who gave some examples. Apparently independently discovered by Bellavitis
in 1836, by Stubbs and Ingram in 1842-3, and by Lord
Kelvin in 1845. The latter employed the idea with con-
spicuous success in his electrical researches.

1. DEFINITION: Consider the circle with center O and
radius k. Two points A and $\overline{A}$, collinear with O, are
<u>mutually</u> <u>inverse</u> <u>with</u> <u>respect</u> <u>to</u>
<u>this circle</u> if

$$(OA)(O\overline{A}) = k^2.$$

In polar coordinates with O as
pole, this relation is

$$r \cdot \rho = k^2 ;$$

in rectangular coordinates:

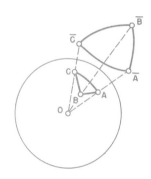

Fig. 122

$$x_1 = \frac{k^2 x}{x^2 + y^2} ; \quad y_1 = \frac{k^2 y}{x^2 + y^2} .$$

(If this product is negative, the points are negatively
inverse and lie on opposite sides of O.)

Two <u>curves</u> are mutually inverse if every point of each
has an inverse belonging to the other.

2. CONSTRUCTION OF INVERSE POINTS:

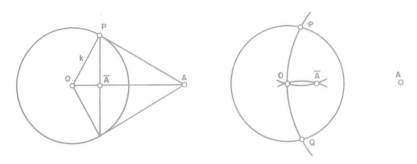

Fig. 123

For the point $\overline{A}$ inverse to A, draw the tangent AP, then from P the perpendicular to OA. From similar right triangles

$$\frac{O\overline{A}}{k} = \frac{k}{OA} \quad \text{or} \quad (OA)(O\overline{A}) = k^2.$$

Compass Construction: Draw the circle through O with center at A, meeting the circle of inversion in P, Q. Circles with centers P and Q through O meet in $\overline{A}$. (For proof, consider the similar isosceles triangles OAP and $PO\overline{A}$.)

3. PROPERTIES:

(a) As A approaches O the distance $O\overline{A}$ increases indefinitely.

(b) Points of the circle of inversion are invariant.

(c) <u>Circles</u> orthogonal to the circle of inversion are invariant.

(d) <u>Angles</u> between two curves are preserved in magnitude but reversed in direction.

(e) <u>Circles</u>:

$$r^2 + A \cdot r \cdot \cos\theta + B \cdot r \cdot \sin\theta + C = 0 = x^2 + y^2 + Ax + By + C$$

invert (by $r\rho = 1$) into the circles:

$$1 + A \cdot \rho \cdot \cos\theta + B \cdot \rho \cdot \sin\theta + C\rho^2 = C(x^2 + y^2) + Ax + By + 1 = 0$$

unless C = 0 (a circle through the origin) in which
case the circle inverts into the Line:

$$1 + A \cdot \rho \cdot \cos\theta + B \cdot \rho \cdot \sin\theta = 1 + Ax + By = 0.$$

(f) <u>Lines</u> through the origin:

$$Ax + By = 0 = A \cdot \cos\theta + B \cdot \sin\theta$$

are <u>unaltered</u>.

(g) <u>Asymptotes</u> of a curve invert into <u>tangents</u> to the
inverse curve at the origin.

4. SOME INVERSIONS: (k = 1)

(a) With center of inversion
at its vertex, a <u>Parabola</u> inverts into the <u>Cissoid</u> <u>of</u>
<u>Diocles</u>.

$$y^2 = hx \longleftrightarrow \frac{y^2}{(x^2 + y^2)} = hx,$$

or $\quad y^2 = \dfrac{hx^3}{(1 - hx)}$.

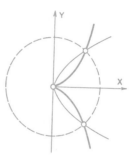

Fig. 124

(b) With center of inversion
at a vertex, the <u>Rectangular</u>
<u>Hyperbola</u> inverts into the
ordinary <u>Strophoid</u>.

$$x^2 - y^2 + 2ax = 0 \longleftrightarrow x^2 - y^2 + 2ax(x^2 + y^2) = 0,$$

or $\quad y^2 = x^2 \cdot \dfrac{1 + 2ax}{1 - 2ax}$.

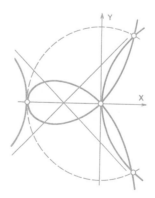

Fig. 125

(c) With center of inversion at its center, the
Rectangular Hyperbola inverts
into a Lemniscate.

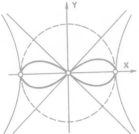

$$r^2 \cos 2\theta = 1 \longleftrightarrow \rho^2 = \cos 2\theta.$$

Fig. 126

(d) With center of inversion at a focus, the Conics
invert into Limacons.

$$r = \frac{1}{(a + b \cdot \cos \theta)} \longleftrightarrow \rho = a + b \cdot \cos \theta.$$

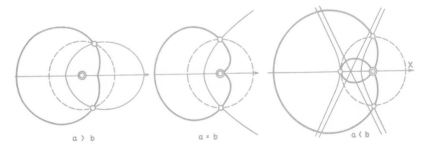

a ⟩ b   a = b   a ⟨ b

Fig. 127

(e) With center of inversion at their center, con-
focal <u>Central</u> <u>Conics</u> invert
into a family of <u>ovals</u> and
"figures eight."

$$\frac{x^2}{(a^2 + \lambda)} + \frac{y^2}{(b^2 + \lambda)} = 1$$

$$\longleftrightarrow \frac{x^2}{(a^2 + \lambda)} + \frac{y^2}{(b^2 + \lambda)} =$$

$$(x^2 + y^2)^2.$$

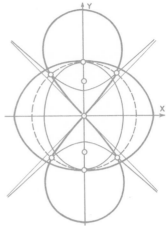

Fig. 128

5. MECHANICAL INVERSORS:

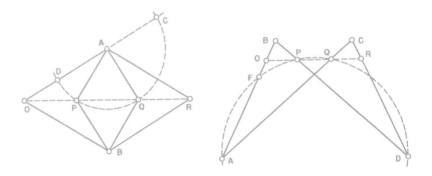

Fig. 129

The <u>Peaucellier</u> <u>Cell</u> (1864), | The <u>Hart</u> <u>Crossed</u> <u>Parallel</u>-
the first mechanical | <u>ogram</u> carries four collinear

inversor, is formed of two rhombuses as shown. Its appearance ended a long search for a machine to convert circular motion into linear motion, a problem that was almost unanimously agreed insoluble. For the inversive property, draw the circle through P with center A. Then, by the secant property of circles,

$$(OP)(OQ) = (OD)(OC)$$

$$= (a-b)(a+b) = a^2 - b^2.$$

Moreover,

$$(PO)(PR) = -(OP)(OQ) = b^2 - a^2$$

if directions be assigned.

points O, P, Q, R taken on a line parallel to the bases AD and BC.* Draw the circle through D, A, P, and Q meeting AB in F. By the secant property of circles,

$$(BF)(BA) = (BP)(BD).$$

Here, the distances BA, BP, and BD are constant and thus BF is constant. Accordingly, as the mechanism is deformed, F is a fixed point of AB. Again,

$$(OP)(OQ) = (OF)(OA) = \text{constant}$$

by virtue of the foregoing. Thus the Hart Cell of four bars is equivalent to the Peaucellier arrangement of eight bars.

For <u>line</u> <u>motion</u>, an extra bar is added to each mechanism to describe a circle through the fixed point (the center of inversion) as shown in Fig. 130.

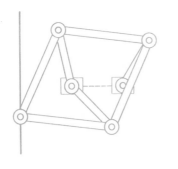
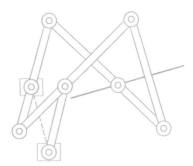

Fig. 130

In each mechanism, the line generated is perpendicular to the line of fixed points.

6. Since the inverse A of Ā lies on the polar of Ā, the subject of inversion is that of
<u>poles</u> <u>and</u> <u>polars</u>, with respect to the given circle. The points O, P, A, and Ā form an harmonic set - that is, A and Ā divide the distance OP in "extreme and mean ratio". A generalization of inversion leads to the theory of polars with respect to curves other than the circle, viz., conics. (See Conics, 6 ff.)

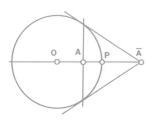

Fig. 131

7. The process of inversion forms an expeditious method of solving a variety of problems. For example, the celebrated problem of Apollonius (see Circles) is to construct a circle tangent to three given circles. If the given circles do not intersect, each radius is increased by a length <u>a</u> so that two are tangent. This point of tangency is taken as center of inversion so that the inverted configuration is composed of two parallel lines and a circle. The circle tangent to these three elements is easily obtained by straightedge and compass. The inverse (with respect to the same circle of inversion) of

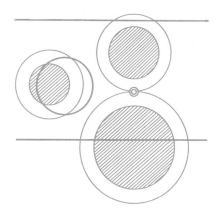

Fig. 132

this circle followed by an alteration of its radius by the length <u>a</u> is the required circle.

8. Inversion is a helpful means of generating theorems or geometrical properties which are otherwise not readily obtainable. For example, consider the elementary theorem: "If two opposite angles of a quadrilateral OABC are supplementary it is cyclic." Let this configuration be inverted with respect to O, sending A, B, C into A̅, B̅, C̅ and their circumcircle into the line A̅C̅. Obviously, B̅ lies on this line. If B be allowed to move upon the circle, B̅ moves upon a line. Thus

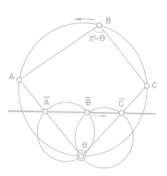

Fig. 133

"The locus of the intersection of circles on the fixed points O,A̅ and O,C̅ meeting at a constant angle (here π - θ) is the line A̅C̅."

BIBLIOGRAPHY

Adler, A.: <u>Geometrischen Konstruktionen</u>, Leipsig (1906) 37 ff.
Courant and Robbins: <u>What is Mathematics?</u> Oxford (1941) 158.
Daus, P. H.: <u>College Geometry</u>, Prentice-Hall (1941) Chap. 3.
Johnson, R. A.: <u>Modern Geometry</u>, Houghton-Mifflin (1929) 43 ff.
Shively, L. S.: <u>Modern Geometry</u>, John Wiley (1939) 80.
Yates, R.C.: <u>Geometrical Tools</u>, Educational Publishers, St. Louis (1949).

INVOLUTES

HISTORY: The Involute of a Circle was discussed and utilized by Huygens in 1693 in connection with his study of clocks without pendulums for service on ships of the sea.

1. DESCRIPTION: An involute of a curve is the roulette of a selected point on a line that rolls (as a tangent) upon the curve. Or, it is the path of a point of a string tautly unwound from the curve. Two facts are evident at once: since the line is at any point normal to the involute, all involutes of a given curve are parallel to each other, Fig. 134(a); further, the evolute of a curve is the envelope of its normals.

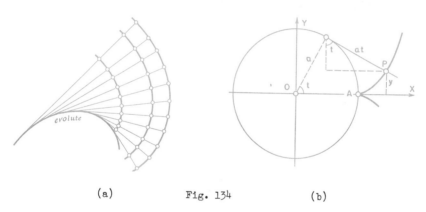

(a)   Fig. 134   (b)

The details that follow pertain only to the Involute of a Circle, Fig. 134(b), a curve interesting for its applications.

2. EQUATIONS:

$$\begin{cases} x = a(\cos t + t \cdot \sin t) \\ y = a(\sin t - t \cdot \cos t) \ . \end{cases}$$

$p^2 = r^2 - a^2$ (with respect to 0). $\sqrt{r^2 - a^2} = a\theta + a \cdot \text{arc } \cos \left(\frac{a}{r}\right)$

$2s = a\phi^2 = at^2$ $R^2 = 2as \ (= a^2 t^2)$.

3. METRICAL PROPERTIES:

$$A = \frac{p^3}{6a} \text{ (bounded by OA, OP, AP).}$$

4. GENERAL ITEMS:

(a) Its normal is tangent to the circle.

(b) It is the locus of the pole of an Equiangular spiral rolling on a circle concentric with the base circle (Maxwell, 1849).

(c) Its pedal with respect to the center of its base circle is a spiral of Archimedes.

(d) It is the locus of the intersection of tangents drawn at the points where any ordinate to OA meets the circle and the corresponding cycloid having its vertex at A.

(e) The limit of a succession of involutes of any given curve is an Equiangular spiral. (See Spirals, Equiangular.)

(f) In 1891, the dome of the Royal Observatory at Greenwich was constructed in the form of the surface of revolution generated by an arc of an involute of a circle. (Mo. Notices Roy. Astr. Soc., v 51, p. 436.)

(g) It is a special case of the Euler Spirals.

(h) The roulette of the center of the attached base circle, as the involute rolls on a line, is a parabola.

(i) Its <u>inverse</u> with respect to the base circle is a <u>spiral tractrix</u> (a curve which in polar coordinates has constant tangent length).

(j) It is used frequently in the design of <u>cams</u>.

(k) Concerning its use in the construction of gear teeth, consider its generation by rolling a circle <u>together with its plane</u> along a line, Fig. 135. The path of a selected point P of the line <u>on the moving plane</u> is the involute of a circle. At any instant the center of rotation of P is the point C of the circle. Thus two circles with fixed centers could have their involutes tangent at P with this point of tangency always on the common internal tangent (the line of action) of the two circles. Accordingly, a constant velocity ratio is transmitted and the fundamental law of gearing is satisfied. Advantages over the older form of cycloidal gear teeth include:

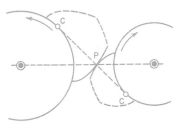

Fig. 135

    1. velocity ratio unaffected by changing distance between centers,
    2. constant pressure on the axes,
    3. single curvature teeth (thus easier cut),
    4. more uniform wear on the teeth.

BIBLIOGRAPHY

<u>American Mathematical Monthly</u>, v 28 (1921) 328.
Byerly, W. E.: <u>Calculus</u>, Ginn (1889) 133.
<u>Encyclopaedia Britannica</u>, 14th Ed., under "Curves, Special".
Huygens, C.: <u>Works</u>, la Société Hollandaise des Sciences (1888) 514.
Keown and Faires: <u>Mechanism</u>, McGraw-Hill (1931) 61, 125.

ISOPTIC CURVES

HISTORY: The origin of the notion of isoptic curves is obscure. Among contributors to the subject will be found the names of Chasles on isoptics of <u>Conics</u> and <u>Epitrochoids</u> (1837) and la Hire on those of Cycloids (1704).

1. DESCRIPTION: The locus of the intersection of tangents to a curve (or curves) meeting at a constant angle α is the <u>Isoptic</u> of the given curve (or curves). If the constant angle be π/2, the isoptic is called the <u>Orthoptic</u>. Isoptic curves are in fact <u>Glissettes</u>.

   A special case of Orthoptics is the <u>Pedal</u> of a curve with respect to a point. (A carpenter's square moves with one edge through the fixed point while the other edge forms a tangent to the curve).

2. ILLUSTRATION: It is well known that the Orthoptic of the Parabola is its directrix while those of the Central Conics are a pair of concentric Circles. These are immediate upon eliminating the parameter <u>m</u> between the equations in the sets of perpendicular tangents that follow:

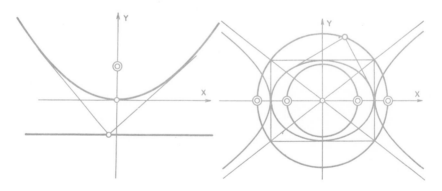

Fig. 136

$$\begin{cases} y - mx \pm \sqrt{a^2 m^2 \pm b^2} = 0 \\ my + x \pm \sqrt{a^2 \pm b^2 m^2} = 0. \end{cases}$$

$$\begin{cases} y - mx + pm^2 = 0 \\ m^2 y + mx + p = 0. \end{cases}$$

(The Orthoptic of the Hyperbola is the circle through the foci of the corresponding Ellipse and vice versa.)

3. GENERAL ITEMS:

(a) The Orthoptic is the envelope of the circle on PQ as a diameter. (Fig. 137)

(b) The locus of the intersection of two perpendicular normals to a curve is the Orthoptic of its Evolute.

(c) <u>Tangent</u> Construction: Fig. 137. Let the normals to the given curve at P and Q meet in H. This is the instantaneous center of rotation of the rigid body formed by the constant angle at R. Thus HR is normal to the Isoptic generated by the point R.

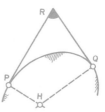

Fig. 137

4. EXAMPLES:

Given Curve	Isoptic Curve
Cycloid Epicycloid Sinusoidal Spiral Two Circles Parabola	Curtate or Prolate Cycloid Epitrochoid Sinusoidal Spiral Limacons (see Glissettes, 4) Hyperbola (same focus and directrix)

Given Curve	Orthoptic Curve
Two Confocal Conics	Concentric Circle
Hypocycloid	$r = (a-2b)\cdot\sin[\frac{a}{(a-2b)}](\frac{\pi}{2} - \theta)$
Deltoid	Its Inscribed Circle
Cardioid	A Circle and a Limacon
Astroid: $x^{\frac{2}{3}} + y^{\frac{2}{3}} = a^{\frac{2}{3}}$	Quadrifolium: $r^2 = (\frac{a^2}{2})\cdot\cos^2 2\theta$
Sinusoidal Spiral: $r^n = a^n \cos n\theta$	Sinusoidal Spiral: $r = a\cdot\cos^k(\frac{\theta}{k})$ where $k = \frac{(n+1)}{n}$
$y^2 = x^3$	$729y^2 = 180x - 16$
$3(x + y) = x^3$	$81y^2(x^2+y^2) - 36(x^2 - 2xy + 5y^2) + 128 = 0$
$x^2y^2 - 4a(x^3 + y^3) + 18a^2xy - 2ya^4 = 0$	$x + y + 2a = 0$
Equiangular Spiral	A Congruent Spiral*

NOTE: The α-Isoptic of the Parabola $y^2 = 4ax$ is the Hyperbola $\tan^2\alpha\cdot(a + x)^2 = y^2 - 4ax$ and those of the Ellipse and Hyperbola: (top and bottom signs resp.):

$$\tan^2\alpha\cdot(x^2 + y^2 - a^2 \mp b^2)^2 = 4(a^2y^2 \pm b^2x^2 \mp a^2b^2).$$

(these include the $\pi - \alpha$ Isoptics).

BIBLIOGRAPHY

Duporcq: L'Interm. d. Math. (1896) 291.
Encyclopaedia Britannica: 14th Ed., "Curves, Special."
Hilton, H.: Plane Algebraic Curves, Oxford (1932) 169.

*See Am. Math. Monthly, v55, 317.

KIEROID

HISTORY: This curve was devised by P. J. Kiernan in 1945 to establish a family relationship among the Conchoid, the Cissoid, and the Strophoid.

1. DESCRIPTION: The center B of the circle of radius a moves along the line BA. O is a fixed point, c units distant from AB. A secant is drawn through O and D, the midpoint of the chord cut from the line DE which is parallel to AB and b units distant. The locus of P_1 and P_2, points of intersection of OD and the circle, is the Kieroid.

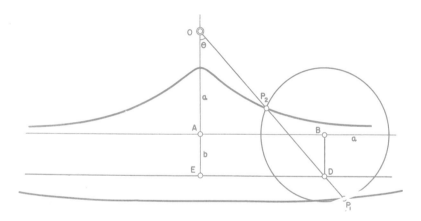

Fig. 138

The curve has a double point if c < a or a cusp if c = a. There are two asymptotes as shown.

2. SPECIAL CASES: Three special cases are of importance:

| If b = 0, the curve is a Con-choid of Nicomedes. | If b = a, the curve is a Cis-soid (plus an asymptote). | If b = a = -c (points O and A coincide), the curve is a Stroph-oid (plus an asymptote). |

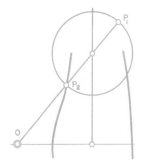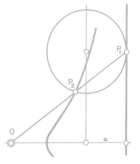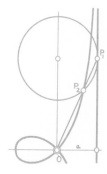

Fig. 139

It is but an exercise to form the equations of these curves after suitable choice of reference axes.

LEMNISCATE OF BERNOULLI

HISTORY: Discovered and discussed by Jacques Bernoulli
in 1694. Also studied by C. Maclaurin. James Watt (1784)
of steam engine fame is responsible for the crossed
parallelogram mechanism given at the end of this section. He used the device for approximate line motion -
thereby reducing the height of his engine house by nine
feet.

1. DESCRIPTION:

The Lemniscate is a special
Cassinian Curve. That is,
it is the locus of a point
P the product of whose distances from two fixed
points F_1, F_2 (the foci) 2a
units apart is constant and
equal to a^2.

It is the Cissoid of the
circle of radius a/2 with
respect to a point 0 dis-
tant $a \sqrt{2}/2$ units from
its center.

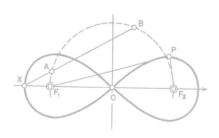 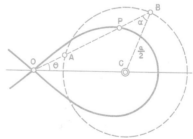

Fig. 140

$$(F_1P)(F_2P) = a^2$$

A Point-wise Construction:
Let OX = $a \sqrt{2}$. Then, by the
secant property of the circle on F_1F_2 as diameter:

$$(XA)(XB) = a^2.$$

Thus, take $F_1P = XB$,
$F_2P = XA$, etc.

$$r = OP = OB - OA = AB.$$

Since $\dfrac{\sin \alpha}{a \sqrt{2}/2} = \dfrac{\sin \theta}{\dfrac{a}{2}}$,

$r = a \cdot \cos \alpha = a \sqrt{(1 - 2\sin^2\theta)}$,
$r^2 = a^2 \cdot \cos 2\theta.$

2. EQUATIONS:

$$r^2 = a^2\cos 2\theta, \qquad \text{or} \qquad r^2 = a^2\sin2\theta, \text{ etc.}$$

$$(x^2 + y^2)^2 = a^2(x^2 - y^2). \qquad (x^2 + y^2)^2 = 2a^2xy.$$

$$r^3 = a^2 \cdot p.$$

3. METRICAL PROPERTIES:

$A = a^2$.

$$L = 4a(1 + \frac{1}{2 \cdot 5} + \frac{1 \cdot 3}{2 \cdot 4 \cdot 9} + \frac{1 \cdot 3 \cdot 5}{2 \cdot 4 \cdot 6 \cdot 13} + \ldots) \text{ (elliptic)}.$$

V (of $r^2 = a^2 \cos 2\theta$ revolved about the polar axis)

$$= 2\pi a^2(2 - \sqrt{2}).$$

$$R = \frac{a^2}{3r} = \frac{r^2}{3p} . \qquad \psi = 2\theta + \frac{\pi}{2} .$$

4. GENERAL ITEMS:

(a) It is the Pedal of a Rectangular Hyperbola with respect to its center.

(b) It is the Inverse of a Rectangular Hyperbola with respect to its center. (The asymptotes of the Hyperbola invert into tangents to the Lemniscate at the origin.)

(c) It is the Sinusoidal Spiral: $r^n = a^n\cos n\theta$ for $n = 2$.

(d) It is the locus of flex points of a family of confocal Cassinian Curves.

(e) It is the envelope of circles with centers on a Rectangular Hyperbola which pass through its center.

(f) <u>Tangent</u> <u>Construction</u>:

Since $\psi = 2\theta + \dfrac{\pi}{2}$, the

<u>normal</u> makes an angle 2θ

with the radius vector

and 3θ with the polar

axis. The tangent is

thus easily constructed.

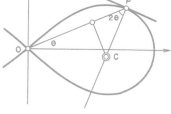

Fig. 141

(g) <u>Radius</u> <u>of</u> <u>Curvature</u>

(Fig. 141) $R = \dfrac{a^2}{3r}$. The

projection of R on the radius vector is

$$R \cdot \cos 2\theta = \left(\frac{a^2}{3r}\right) \cdot \cos 2\theta = \frac{r}{3} \; .$$

Thus <u>the</u> <u>perpendicular</u> <u>to</u> <u>the</u> <u>radius</u> <u>vector</u> <u>at</u> <u>its</u> <u>trisection</u> <u>point</u> <u>farthest</u> <u>from</u> <u>O</u> <u>meets</u> <u>the</u> <u>normal</u> <u>in</u> <u>C</u>, <u>the</u> <u>center</u> <u>of</u> <u>curvature</u>.

(h) It is the path of a body acted upon by a central force varying inversely as the seventh power of the distance. (See Spirals 2g and 3f.)

(j) <u>Generation</u> <u>by</u> <u>Linkages</u>:

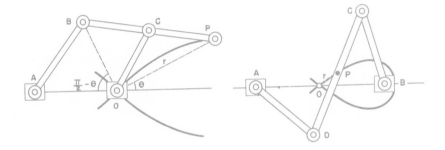

Fig. 142

$OA = AB = a;$ $BC = CP = OC = \dfrac{a}{\sqrt{2}}$.

Since angle $BOP = \dfrac{\pi}{2}$ always,

$r^2 = (BP)^2 - (OB)^2 =$

$\qquad 2a^2 - 4a^2 \sin^2 \theta,$

or $\quad r^2 = 2a^2 \cos 2\theta.$

$AB = CD = a \sqrt{2}$.

$AD = BC = a.$

P and 0 are midpoints of
DC and AB, resp.

$r^2 = a^2 \cos 2\theta,$

(See <u>Tools</u>.)

BIBLIOGRAPHY

Encyclopaedia Britannica: 14th Ed., "Curves, Special."
Hilton, H.: Plane Algebraic Curves, Oxford (1932).
Phillips, A. W.: Linkwork for the Lemniscate, Am. J.
    Math. I (1878) 386.
Wieleitner, H.: Spezielle ebene Kurven, Leipsig (1908).
Williamson, B.: Differential Calculus, Longmans, Green
    (1895).
Yates, R.C.: Geometrical Tools, Educational Publishers,
    St. Louis (1949) 172.

LIMACON OF PASCAL

HISTORY: Discovered by Etienne (father of Blaise) Pascal and discussed by Roberval in 1650.

1. DESCRIPTION:

It is the Epitrochoid generated by a point rigidly attached to a circle rolling upon an equal fixed circle.

It is the Conchoid of a circle where the fixed point is on the circle.

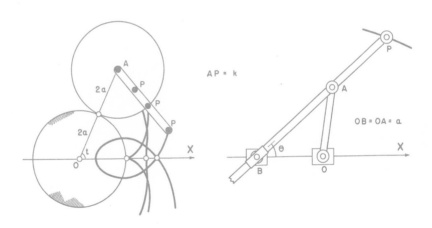

Fig. 143

Cusp if 2a = k;   Double Point: 2a < k;   Indentation: 2a > k.

2. EQUATIONS:

$$x = 4a \cdot \cos t - k \cdot \cos 2t \qquad r = 2a \cdot \cos\theta + k.$$
$$y = 4a \cdot \sin t - k \cdot \sin 2t$$

$$(x^2 + y^2 - 2ax)^2 = k^2(x^2 + y^2),$$

(origin at singular point).

3. GENERAL ITEMS:

(a) It is the <u>Pedal</u> of a circle with respect to any point. (If the point is on the circle, the pedal is the Cardioid.) (For a mechanical description, see Tools, p. 188.)

(b) Its Evolute is the <u>Catacaustic</u> of a circle for any point source of light.

(c) It is the <u>Glissette</u> of a selected point of an invariable triangle which slides between two fixed points.

(d) The locus of any point rigidly attached to a constant angle whose sides touch two fixed circles is a pair of Limacons (see Glissettes 2a and 4).

(e) It is the <u>Inverse</u> of a conic with respect to a focus. (The inverse of $r = 2a \cdot \cos\theta + k$ is $r(2a \cdot \cos\theta + k) = 0$, an Ellipse, Parabola, or Hyperbola according as $2a < k$, $2a = k$, $2a > k$). (See Inversion 4d.)

(f) It is a special <u>Cartesian Oval</u>.

(g) It is part of the <u>Orthoptic</u> of a <u>Cardioid</u>.

(h) It is the <u>Trisectrix</u> if $k = a$. The angle formed by the axis and the line joining (a,o) with any point (r,θ) of the curve is 3θ. (Not to be confused with the Trisectrix of Maclaurin which resembles the Folium of Descartes.)

(i) <u>Tangent</u> <u>Construction</u>:

The point A of the bar has direction perpendicular to OA while the point of the bar at B has the direction of the bar itself. The normals to these directions meet in H, a point of the circle. Accordingly, HP is normal to the path of P and its perpendicular there is a tangent to the curve.

Since T is the center of rotation of any point rigidly attached to the rolling circle, TP is normal to the path of P and its perpendicular at P is a tangent.

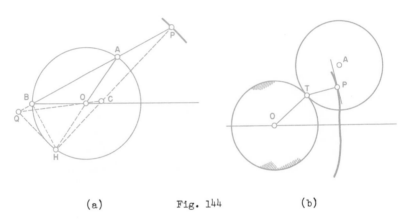

(a)   Fig. 144   (b)

(j) <u>Radius</u> <u>of</u> <u>Curvature</u>: $R = \dfrac{(2a \pm k)^2}{(4a \pm k)}$.

The center of curvature is at C, Fig. 144(a). Draw HQ perpendicular to HP until it meets AB in Q. C is the intersection of QO and HP.

(k) <u>Double</u> <u>Generation</u>: (See Epicycloids.) It may also be generated by a point attached to a circle rolling <u>internally</u> (centers on the same side of the common tangent) to a fixed circle half the size of the rolling circle.

(1) The Limacon may be generated by the following
linkage: CDKF and CGED
are two similar (pro-
portional) crossed
parallelograms with
points C and F fixed
to the plane. CHJD is
a parallelogram and P
is a point on the ex-
tension of JD. The
action here is that
produced by a circle
with center D roll-
ing upon an equal
fixed circle whose
center is C. The
locus of P (or any
point rigidly at-
tached to JD) is a
Limacon. (See an
equivalent mechanism
under Cardioid.)

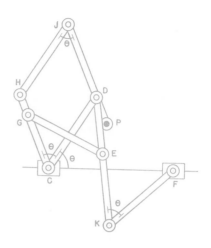

Fig. 145

BIBLIOGRAPHY

Edwards, J.: Calculus, Macmillan (1892) 349.
Salmon, G.: Higher Plane Curves, Dublin (1879).
Wieleitner, H.: Spezielle ebene Kurven, Leipsig (1908)
    88.
Yates, R.C.: Geometrical Tools, Educational Publishers
    St. Louis (1949) 182.

NEPHROID

HISTORY: Studied by Huygens and Tschirnhausen about 1679 in connection with the theory of caustics. Jacques Bernoulli in 1692 showed that the Nephroid is the catacaustic of a cardioid for a luminous cusp. Double generation was first discovered by Daniel Bernoulli in 1725.

1. DESCRIPTION: The Nephroid is a 2-cusped Epicycloid. The rolling circle may be one-half (a = 2b) or three-halves (3a = 2b) the radius of the fixed circle.

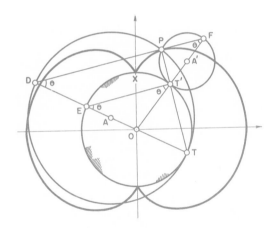

Fig. 146

For this double generation, let the fixed circle have center O and radius OT = OE = a, and the rolling circle center A' and radius A'T' = A'F = a/2, the latter carrying the tracing point P. Draw ET', OT'F, and PT' to T Let D be the intersection of TO and FP and draw the circle on T, P, and D. This circle is tangent to the fixed circle since angle DPT = $\pi/2$. Now since PD is parallel to T'E, triangles OET' and OFD are isosceles and thus

$$TD = 3a.$$

Furthermore, arc TT' = 2aθ and arc T'P = aθ = arc T'X.

Thus   arc TX = 3aθ = arc TP.

Accordingly, if P were attached to either rolling circle - the one of radius a/2 or the one of radius 3a/2 - the same Nephroid would be generated.

2. EQUATIONS: (a = 2b) .

$$\begin{cases} x = b(3\cos t - \cos 3t) \\ y = b(3\sin t - \sin 3t) \end{cases} \cdot \quad (x^2 + y^2 - 4a^2)^3 = 108a^4y^2 .$$

$$s = 6b \cdot \sin(\tfrac{\varphi}{2}). \qquad\qquad 4R^2 + s^2 = 36b^2.$$

$$p = 4b \cdot \sin(\tfrac{\varphi}{2}). \qquad\qquad r^2 = 4b^2 + \frac{3p^2}{4}.$$

$$(r/2)^{\frac{2}{3}} = a^{\frac{2}{3}} \cdot [\sin^{\frac{2}{3}}(\tfrac{\theta}{2}) + \cos^{\frac{2}{3}}(\tfrac{\theta}{2})].$$

$$x \cdot \cos\varphi + y \cdot \sin\varphi = 4b \cdot \sin(\tfrac{\varphi}{2}).$$

3. METRICAL PROPERTIES: (a = 2b).

$$L = 24b. \qquad\qquad A = 12\pi b^2. \qquad\qquad R = \frac{3p}{4} .$$

4. GENERAL ITEMS:

   (a) It is the catacaustic of a Cardioid for a luminous cusp.

   (b) It is the catacaustic of a Circle for a set of parallel rays.

   (c) Its evolute is another Nephroid.

   (d) It is the evolute of a Cayley Sextic (a curve parallel to the Nephroid).

   (e) It is the envelope of a diameter of the circle that generates a Cardioid.

   (f) Tangent Construction: Since T' (or T) is the instantaneous center of rotation of P, the normal is T'P and the tangent therefore PF (or PD). (Fig. 151.)

BIBLIOGRAPHY

Edwards, J.: <u>Calculus</u>, Macmillan (1892) 343 ff.
Proctor, R. A.: <u>A Treatise on the Cycloid</u> (1878).
Wieleitner, H.: <u>Spezielle ebene Kurven</u>, Leipsig (1908)
   139 ff.

PARALLEL CURVES

HISTORY: Leibnitz was the first to consider Parallel Curves in 1692-4, prompted no doubt by the Involutes of Huygens (1673).

1. DEFINITION: Let P be a variable point on a given curve. The locus of Q and Q', $\pm$ k units distant from P measured along the normal, is a curve parallel to the given curve. There are two branches.

For some values of k, a Parallel curve may not be unlike the given curve in appearance, but for other values of k it may be totally dissimilar. Notice the paths of a pair of wheels with the axle perpendicular to their planes.

Fig. 147

2. GENERAL ITEMS:

(a) Since Parallel Curves have common normals, they have a common Evolute.

(b) The tangent to the given curve at P is parallel to the tangent at Q. A Parallel Curve then is the envelope of lines:

$$ax + by + c = \pm \, k \cdot \sqrt{a^2 + b^2} \, ,$$

distant $\pm$ k units from the tangent: $ax + by + c = 0$ to the given curve.

(c) A Parallel Curve is the envelope of circles of radius k whose centers lie on the given curve. This affords a rather effective means of sketching various parallel curves.

PARALLEL CURVES

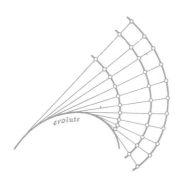

(d) All Involutes of a given curve are parallel to each other (Fig. 148).

Fig. 148

(e) The difference in lengths of two branches of a Parallel Curve is $4\pi k$.

3. SOME EXAMPLES: Illustrations selected from familiar curves follow.

(a) Curves parallel to the Parabola are of the 6th degree; those parallel to the Central Conics are of the 8th degree. (See Salmon's Conics).

(b) The Astroid $x^{\frac{2}{3}} + y^{\frac{2}{3}} = a^{\frac{2}{3}}$ has parallel curves:

$$[\,3(x^2 + y^2 - a^2) - 4k^2\,]^3 + [\,27axy - 9k(x^2 + y^2) - 18a^2k + 8k^3\,]^2 = 0.$$

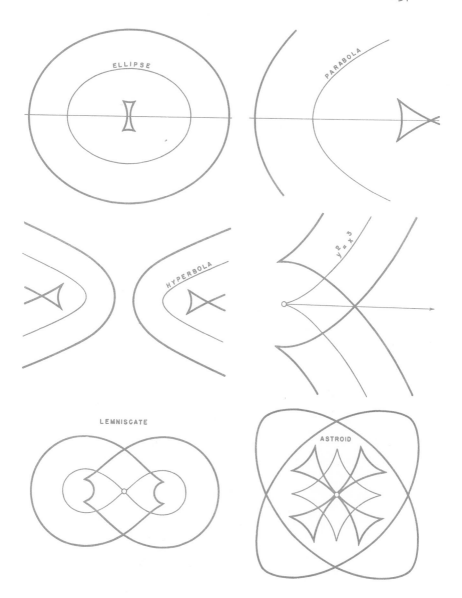

Fig. 149

4. A LINKAGE FOR CURVES PARALLEL TO THE ELLIPSE:

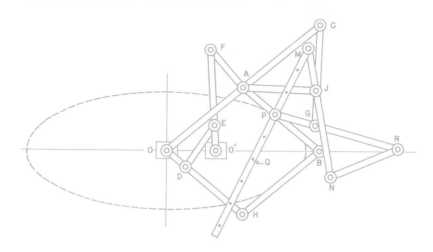

Fig. 150

A straight line mechanism is built from two <u>proportional</u> crossed parallelograms OO'EDO and OO'FAO. The rhombus on OA and OH is completed to B. Since OO' (here the plane on which the motion takes place) always bisects angle AOH, the point B travels along the line OO'. (See Tools, p. 96.) Any point P then describes an Ellipse with semi-axes equal in length to OA + AP and PB.

Since A moves on a circle with center O, and B moves along the line OO', the instantaneous center of rotation of P is the intersection C of OA produced and the perpendicular to OO' at B. This point C then lies on a circle with center O and radius twice OA.

The "kite" CAPG is completed with AP = PG and CA = CG. Two additional crossed parallelograms APMJA and PMNRP are attached in order to have PM bisect angle APG and to insure that PM be always directed toward C. Thus PM is normal to the path of P and any point such as Q describes a curve parallel to the Ellipse.

BIBLIOGRAPHY

Dienger: Arch. der Math. IX (1847).
Loria, G.: Spezielle Algebraische und Transzendente
   ebene Kurven, Leipsig (1902).
Salmon, G.: Conic Sections, Longmans, Green (1879) 337;
   Par. 372, Ex. 2.
Wieleitner, H.: Spezielle ebene Kurven, Leipsig (1908).
Yates, R. C.: American Mathametical Monthly (1938) 607.

PEDAL CURVES

HISTORY: The idea of positive and negative pedal curves occurred first to Colin Maclaurin in 1718; the name 'Pedal' is due to Terquem. The theory of Caustic Curves includes Pedals in an important role: the <u>orthotomic</u> is an enlargement of the pedal of the reflecting curve with respect to the point source of light (Quetelet, 1822). (See Caustics.) The notion may be enlarged upon to include loci formed by dropping perpendiculars upon a line making a constant angle with the tangent - viz., pedals formed upon the normals to a curve.

1. DESCRIPTION: The locus C_1, Fig. 151(a), of the foot of the perpendicular from a fixed point P (the Pedal Point) upon the tangent to a given curve C is the <u>First Positive Pedal</u> of C with respect to the fixed point. The given curve C is the <u>First Negative Pedal</u> of C_1.

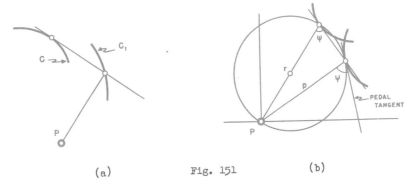

(a)   Fig. 151   (b)

It is shown elsewhere (see Pedal Equations, 5) that the angle ψ between the tangent to a given curve and the radius vector r from the pedal point, Fig. 151(b), equals the corresponding angle for the Pedal Curve. Thus the tangent to the Pedal is also tangent to the circle on r as a diameter. Accordingly, <u>the envelope of these circles is the first positive pedal</u>.

Conversely, the first negative Pedal is then the envelope of the line through a variable point of the curve perpendicular to the radius vector from the Pedal point.

2. RECTANGULAR EQUATIONS: If the given curve be $f(x,y) = 0$, the equation of the Pedal with respect to the origin is the result of eliminating m between the line:

$$y = mx + k$$

and its perpendicular from the origin: $my + x = 0$, where $\underline{k}$ is determined so that the line is tangent to the curve. For example:

The Pedal of the Parabola $y^2 = 2x$ with respect to its vertex $(0,0)$ is

$$\begin{cases} y = mx + \dfrac{1}{2m} \\[2mm] my + x = 0 \end{cases} \quad \text{or} \quad y^2 = -\dfrac{2x^3}{2x + 1}, \quad \text{a \underline{Cissoid}.}$$

3. POLAR EQUATIONS: If (r_0, θ_0) are the coordinates of the foot of the perpendicular from the pole:

$$\tan \psi = r\left(\dfrac{d\theta}{dr}\right), \quad r_0 = r \cdot \sin \psi$$

and

$$\psi + (\theta - \theta_0) = \dfrac{\pi}{2}.$$

Thus $\dfrac{r^2}{r_0{}^2} = 1 + \left(\dfrac{1}{r^2}\right)\left(\dfrac{dr}{d\theta}\right)^2.$

Among these relations, r, θ and ψ may be eliminated to give the polar equation of the pedal curve with respect to the origin.

Fig. 152

For example, consider the Sinusoidal Spirals $r^n = a^n \cos n\theta$.* Differentiating: $n\left(\dfrac{r'}{r}\right) = -n \cdot \tan n\theta$

$= n \cdot \cot \psi$; thus $\psi = \dfrac{\pi}{2} + n\theta.$

---

* Rectifiable when $\dfrac{1}{n}$ is an integer.

But $\theta = \theta_0 + \dfrac{\pi}{2} - \psi = \theta_0 - n\theta$ and thus $\theta = \dfrac{\theta_0}{(n+1)}$.

Now $r_0 = r \cdot \sin \psi = r \cdot \cos n\theta = a \cdot \cos^{\frac{1}{n}} n\theta \cdot \cos n\theta$,

or $r_0 = a \cdot \cos^{(n+1)/n} n\theta = a \cdot \cos^{(n+1)/n}[\dfrac{n\theta_0}{(n+1)}]$.

Thus, dropping subscripts, the first pedal with respect to the pole is:

$$r^{n_1} = a^{n_1}\cos n_1\theta \quad \text{where} \quad n_1 = \dfrac{n}{(n+1)} ,$$

another Sinusoidal Spiral. The iteration is clear. The kth positive pedal is thus

$$\boxed{r^{n_k} = a^{n_k}\cos n_k\theta} \quad \text{where} \quad n_k = \dfrac{n}{(kn+1)}$$

Many of the results given in the table that follows can be read directly from this last equation. (See also Spirals 3, Pedal Equations 6.)

4. PEDAL EQUATIONS OF PEDALS: Let the given curve be $r = f(p)$ and let p_1 denote the perpendicular from the origin upon the tangent to the pedal. Then (See Pedal Equations):

$$p^2 = r \cdot p_1 = f(p) \cdot p_1.$$

Thus, replacing p and p_1 by their respective analogs r and p, the pedal equation of the pedal is:

$$\boxed{r^2 = f(r) \cdot p .}$$

Fig. 153

Thus consider the circle $r^2 = ap$. Here $f(p) = \sqrt{ap}$ and $f(r) = \sqrt{(ar)}$. Hence, the pedal equation of its Pedal with respect to a point on the circle is

$$\boxed{r^2 = \sqrt{(ar)} \cdot p} \quad \text{or} \quad \boxed{r^3 = ap^2} ,$$

a Cardioid. (See Pedal Equations, 6.)

Equations of successive pedals are formed in similar fashion.

5. SOME CURVES AND THEIR PEDALS:

Given Curve	Pedal Point	First Positive Pedal
Circle	Any Point	Limacon
Circle	Point on Circle	Cardioid
Parabola	Vertex	Cissoid
Parabola	Focus	Tangent at Vertex ⎤
Central Conic	Focus	Auxiliary Circle ⎦ See Conics, 16.
Central Conic	Center	$r^2 = A + B \cdot \cos 2\theta$
Rectangular Hyperbola	Center	Lemniscate
Equiangular Spiral	Pole	Equiangular Spiral
Cardioid ($p^2 a = r^3$)	Pole (Cusp)	Cayley's Sextic ($r^4 = ap^3$)
Lemniscate ($pa^2 = r^3$)	Pole	$r^5 = ap^3$
Catacaustic of a Parabola for rays perpendicular to its axis $r \cdot \cos^3(\frac{\theta}{3}) = a$	Pole	Parabola
Sinusoidal Spiral ($r^{n+1} = a^n p$)	Pole	Sinusoidal Spiral
Astroid: $x^{\frac{2}{3}} + y^{\frac{2}{3}} = a^{\frac{2}{3}}$	Center	$2r = \pm a \cdot \sin 2\theta$ (Quadrifolium)
Parabola	Foot of Directrix	Right Strophoid
Parabola	Arb. Point of Directrix	Strophoid
Parabola	Reflection of Focus in Directrix	Trisectrix of Maclaurin
Cissoid	Ordinary Focus	Cardioid
Epi- and Hypocycloids	Center	Roses

(Table Continued)

Given Curve	Pedal Point	First Positive Pedal
Deltoid *	Cusp	Simple Folium
Deltoid	Vertex	Double Folium
Deltoid	Center	Trifolium
Involute of a Circle	Center of Circle	Archimedian Spiral
$x^3 + y^3 = a^3$	Origin	$(x^2 + y^2)^{\frac{3}{2}} = a^{\frac{3}{2}}(x^{\frac{3}{2}} + y^{\frac{3}{2}})$
$x^m y^n = a^{m+n}$	Origin	$r^{n+m} = a^{m+n} \cdot \dfrac{(m+n)^{m+n}}{m^m n^n} \cdot \cos^m\theta \sin^n\theta$
$(\dfrac{x}{a})^n + (\dfrac{y}{b})^n = 1$ (Lamé Curve)	Origin	$(ax)^{n/(n-1)} + (by)^{n/(n-1)} = (x^2 + y^2)^{n/(n-1)}$
(which for n = 2 is an <u>Ellipse</u>; for n = 1/2 a <u>Parabola</u>).		

*
Its pedal with respect to (b,0) has the equation:

$$[(x - b)^2 + y^2] \cdot [y^2 + x(x-b)] = 4a(x - b)y^2,$$

where $x^2 + y^2 = 9a^2$ is the circumcircle of the Deltoid.

6. MISCELLANEOUS ITEMS:

(a) The 4th negative pedal of the Cardioid with respect to its cusp is a <u>Parabola</u>.

(b) The 4th positive pedal of $r^{\frac{2}{9}}\cos(\frac{2}{9})\theta = a^{\frac{2}{9}}$ with respect to the pole is a <u>Rectangular</u> <u>Hyperbola</u>.

(c) $R'(2r^2 - pR) = r^3$ where R, R' are radii of curvature of a curve and its Pedal at corresponding points.

BIBLIOGRAPHY

Edwards, J.: <u>Calculus</u>, Macmillan (1892) 163 ff.
<u>Encyclopaedia</u> <u>Britannica</u>: 14th Ed., under "Curves,
   Special."
Hilton, H.: <u>Plane</u> <u>Alg</u>. <u>Curves</u>, Oxford (1932) 166 ff.
Salmon, G.: <u>Higher</u> <u>Plane</u> <u>Curves</u>, Dublin (1879) 99 ff.
Wieleitner, H.: <u>Spezielle</u> <u>ebene</u> <u>Kurven</u>, Leipsig (1908)
   101 etc.
Williamson, B.: <u>Calculus</u>, Longmans, Green (1895) 224 ff.

PEDAL EQUATIONS

1. DEFINITION: Certain curves have simple equations when expressed in terms of a radius vector r from a selected fixed point and the perpendicular distance p upon the variable tangent to the curve. Such relations are called Pedal Equations.

2. FROM RECTANGULAR TO PEDAL EQUATION: If the given curve be in rectangular coordinates, the pedal equation may be established among the equations of the curve, its tangent, and the perpendicular from the selected point. That is, with

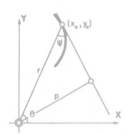

Fig. 154

$$\begin{cases} f(x_0, y_0) = 0, \\ (f_y)_0(y - y_0) + (f_x)_0(x - x_0) = 0, \\ p^2 = \dfrac{[x_0(f_x)_0 + y_0(f_y)_0]^2}{[(f_x)_0^2 + (f_y)_0^2]}, \quad r^2 = x_0^2 + y_0^2, \end{cases}$$

where the pedal point is taken as the origin.

3. FROM POLAR TO PEDAL EQUATION:

Among the relations: $r = f(\theta)$, $p = r \cdot \sin \psi$, $\tan \psi = \dfrac{r}{r'}$, where the selected point is the origin of coordinates, θ and ψ may be eliminated to produce the pedal equation. (For example, see 6.)

4. CURVATURE IN PEDAL COORDINATES: The expression for
radius of curvature is strikingly simple:

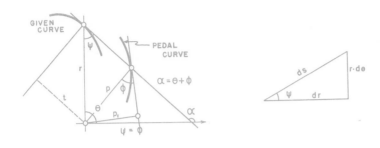

Fig. 155

Since $ds^2 = dr^2 + r^2d\theta^2$ and $\tan\psi = \dfrac{r}{r'} = r(\dfrac{d\theta}{dr})$,

$t = r(\dfrac{dr}{ds}) = p\cdot(\dfrac{dr}{d\theta})/r$ and thus $\underline{d\theta/ds = p/r^2}$

Now $p = r\cdot\sin\psi$ and $dp = (\sin\psi)dr + r(\cos\psi)d\psi$,

or $\dfrac{dp}{ds} = (\dfrac{p}{r})(\dfrac{dr}{ds}) + t(\dfrac{d\psi}{ds})$.

Thus $\dfrac{d\psi}{ds} = (\dfrac{1}{r})(\dfrac{dp}{dr}) - \dfrac{p}{r^2}$.

Accordingly, $K = \dfrac{d\alpha}{ds} = \dfrac{d\psi}{ds} + \dfrac{d\theta}{ds} = (\dfrac{1}{r})(\dfrac{dp}{dr})$ or

$$\boxed{R = r(\dfrac{dr}{dp}).}$$

5. PEDAL EQUATIONS OF PEDAL CURVES: Let the pedal equation of a given curve be $r = f(p)$. If p_1 be the perpendicular upon the tangent to the first positive pedal of
the given curve, then, since p makes an angle of

$\alpha - \dfrac{\pi}{2}$ with the axis of coordinates,

$$\tan\emptyset = p(\dfrac{d\alpha}{dp}) \quad (\text{see Fig. 155}).$$

Now $\tan \varphi(\frac{dp}{ds}) = r \cdot \sin \psi \cdot (\frac{1}{r})(\frac{dp}{dr})$

and thus $\tan \varphi = \sin \psi \cdot (\frac{ds}{dr}) = \tan \psi$.

Accordingly, $\varphi = \psi$ and $p^2 = r \cdot p_1$.

In this last relation, p and p_1 play the same roles as do r and p respectively for the given curve. Thus the pedal equation of the first positive pedal of $r = f(p)$ is

$$\boxed{r^2 = p \cdot f(r)}.$$

Equations of successive Pedal curves are obtained in the same fashion.

6. EXAMPLES: The Sinusoidal Spirals are $\boxed{r^n = a^n \sin n\theta}$. Here,

$$\frac{r}{r'} = \tan n\theta = \tan \psi.$$

Thus $\psi = n\theta$, a relation giving the construction of tangents to various curves of the family.

$$p = r \cdot \sin \psi = r \cdot \sin n\theta = \frac{r^{n+1}}{a^n},$$

or $\boxed{a^n \cdot p = r^{n+1}}$, the pedal equation of the given curve. Special members of this family are included in the following table:

n	$r^n = a^n \sin n\theta$	Curve	Pedal Equation	$R = \frac{a^n}{(n+1)r^{n-1}} = \frac{r^2}{(n+1)p}$
-2	$r^2 \sin 2\theta + a^2 = 0$	Rect.Hyperbola	$rp = a^2$	$-r^3/a^2$
-1	$r \cdot \sin \theta + a = 0$	Line	$p = a$	∞
-1/2	$r = \frac{2a}{1-\cos \theta}$	Parabola	$p^2 = ar$	$2\sqrt{r^3/a}$
+1/2	$r = (\frac{a}{2})(1-\cos \theta)$	Cardioid	$p^2 a = r^3$	$(\frac{2}{3})\sqrt{ar}$
+1	$r = a \cdot \sin \theta$	Circle	$pa = r^2$	$\frac{a}{2}$
+2	$r^2 = a^2 \sin 2\theta$	Lemniscate	$pa^2 = r^3$	$\frac{a^2}{3r}$

(See also Spirals, 3 and Pedal Curves, 3.)

Other curves and corresponding pedal equations are given:

CURVE	PEDAL POINT	PEDAL EQUATION
Parabola (LR = 4a)	Vertex	$a^2(r^2-p^2)^2 = p^2(r^2+4a^2)(p^2+4a^2)$
Ellipse	Focus	$\dfrac{b^2}{p^2} = \dfrac{2a}{r} - 1$
Ellipse	Center	$\dfrac{a^2b^2}{p^2} + r^2 = a^2 + b^2$
Hyperbola	Focus	$\dfrac{b^2}{p^2} = \dfrac{2a}{r} + 1$
Hyperbola	Center	$\dfrac{a^2b^2}{p^2} - r^2 = -a^2 + b^2$
Epi- and Hypocycloids	Center	$p^2 = Ar^2 + B$ **
Astroid	Center	$r^2 + 3p^2 = a^2$
Equiangular (α) Spiral	Pole	$p = r \cdot \sin \alpha$
Deltoid	Center	$8p^2 + 9r^2 = a^2$
Cotes' Spirals	Pole	$\dfrac{1}{p^2} = \dfrac{A}{r^2} + B$
$r^m = a^m\theta$ * (Sacchi 1854)	Pole	$p^2(m^2 \cdot r^{2m} + a^{2m}) = m^2 \cdot r^{2m+2}$

* m = 1:Archimedean Spiral;   m = 2:Fermat's Spiral;
  m = -1:Hyperbolic Spiral;   m = - 2:Lituus.

** $A = \dfrac{(a + 2b)^2}{4b(a + b)}$, $B = -a^2 A.$

BIBLIOGRAPHY

Edwards, J.: <u>Calculus</u>, Macmillan (1892) 161.
<u>Encyclopaedia Britannica</u>, 14th Ed., under "Curves, Special."
Wieleitner, H.: <u>Spezielle ebene Kurven</u> (1908) under "Fusspunkts kurven."
Williamson, B.: <u>Calculus</u>, Longmans, Green (1895) 227 ff.

PURSUIT CURVE

HISTORY: Credited by some to Leonardo da Vinci, it was probably first conceived and solved by Bouguer in 1732.

1. DESCRIPTION: One particle travels along a specified curve while another pursues it, its motion being always directed toward the first particle with related velocities.

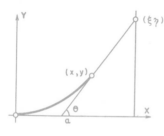

Fig. 156

If the pursuing particle is assigned coordinates (x,y) and there is a function g relating the two velocities $\dfrac{ds}{dt}$, $\dfrac{d\sigma}{dt}$, then the three conditions

$$f(\xi, \eta) = 0; \quad \frac{(\eta - y)}{(\xi - x)} = y';$$

$$g\left(\frac{ds}{dt}, \frac{d\sigma}{dt}\right) = 0,$$

among which ξ, η (coordinates of the pursued particle) may be eliminated, are sufficient to produce the differential equation of the curve of pursuit.

2. SPECIAL CASE: Let the particle pursued travel from rest at the x-axis along the line $x = a$, Fig. 156. The pursuer starts at the same time from the origin with velocity k times the former. Then

$$\xi = a, \quad \frac{(\eta - y)}{(a - x)} = y' \quad \text{or} \quad \eta = y + (a-x)y'$$

$$ds = k \cdot d\sigma \qquad \text{or} \quad dx^2 + dy^2 = k^2 \cdot d\eta^2$$

There follows: $\quad dx^2 + dy^2 = k^2 \cdot [dy - y'dx + (a - x)dy']^2$

$$= k^2(a - x)^2(dy')^2$$

or $\qquad \boxed{1 + y'^2 = k^2(a - x)^2 y''^2}$,

(a differential equation solvable by first setting $y' = p$). Its solutions are

$$2y = \frac{ka^{1/k}(a-x)^{(k-1)/k}}{1-k} + \frac{ka^{-1/k}(a-x)^{(k+1)/k}}{1+k} - \frac{2ka}{1-k^2}, \text{ if } k \neq 1;$$

$$\pm 4ay = (a-x)^2 - 2a^2 \ln\frac{a-x}{a} - a^2, \text{ if } k = 1.$$

The special case when $k = 2$ is the cubic with a loop:

$$a(3y - 2a)^2 = (a-x)(x+2a)^2.$$

3. GENERAL ITEMS:

(a) A much more difficult problem than the special case given above is that where the pursued particle travels on a circle. It seems not to have been solved until 1921 (F. V. Morley and A. S. Hathaway).

(b) There is an interesting case in which three dogs at the vertices of a triangle begin simultaneously to chase one another with equal velocities. The path of each dog is an Equiangular Spiral. (E. Lucas and H. Brocard, 1877).

(c) Since the velocities of the two particles are given, the curves defined by the differential equation in (2) are all rectifiable. It is an interesting exercise to establish this from the differential equation.

BIBLIOGRAPHY

American Mathematical Monthly, v 28, (1921) 54, 91, 278.
Cohen, A.: Differential Equations, D. C. Heath (1933) 173.
Encyclopaedia Britannica, 14th Ed., under "Curves, Special."
Johns Hopkins Univ. Circ., (1908) 135.
Luterbacher, J.: Dissertation, Bern (1900).
Mathematical Gazette (1930-1) 436.
Nouv. Corresp. Math. v 3 (1877) 175, 280.

RADIAL CURVES

HISTORY: The idea of Radial Curves apparently occurred first to Tucker in 1864.

1. DEFINITION: Lines are drawn from a selected point O equal and parallel to the radii of curvature of a given curve. The locus of the end points of these lines is the Radial of the given curve.

2. ILLUSTRATIONS:

(a) The radius of curvature of the Cycloid (Fig. 157(a) (see Cycloid) is (R has inclination $\pi - \dfrac{t}{2} = \theta$):

$$R = 2(PH) = 4a \cdot \sin(\tfrac{t}{2}).$$

Thus, if the fixed point be taken at a cusp, the radial curve in polar coordinates is:

$$\boxed{r = 4a \cdot \sin(\tfrac{t}{2}) = 4a \cdot \sin \theta}$$

a circle of radius 2a.

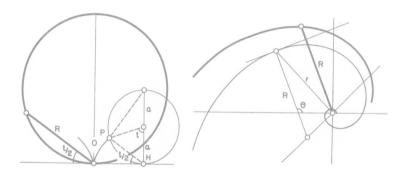

(a) Fig. 157 (b)

(b) The Equiangular Spiral $s = a(e^{m\varphi} - 1)$ Fig. 157(b)
has $R = m \cdot a \cdot e^{m\varphi}$. Thus, if θ be the inclination of the
radius of curvature, $\theta = \dfrac{\pi}{2} + \varphi$, and

$$r = m \cdot a \cdot e^{m(\theta - \pi/2)}$$

is the polar equation of the Radial: another Equiangular Spiral.

3. RADIAL CURVES OF THE CONICS:

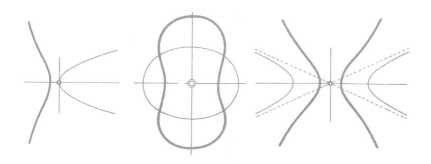

Fig. 158

$$x^3 = \pm k \cdot (x^2 + y^2) \qquad\qquad (a^2x^2 + b^2y^2)^3 = a^4b^4(x^2 + y^2)^2$$

$$[\text{Ellipse} : b^2 > 0;$$

$$\text{Hyperbola}: b^2 < 0].$$

4. GENERAL ITEMS:

(a) The degree of the Radial of an algebraic curve is
the same as that of the curve's Evolute.

RADIAL CURVES

5. EXAMPLES:

Curve	Radial
Ordinary Catenary	Kampyle of Eudoxus
Catenary of Un.Str.	Straight Line
Tractrix	Kappa Curve
Cycloid	Circle
Epicycloid	Roses
Deltoid	Trifolium
Astroid	Quadrifolium

BIBLIOGRAPHY

Encyclopaedia Britannica: 14th Ed., "Curves, Special."
Tucker: Proc. Lon. Math. Soc., 1, (1865).
Wieleitner, H.: Spezielle ebene Kurven, Leipsig (1908) 362.

ROULETTES

HISTORY: Besant in 1869 seems to have been the first to give any sort of systematic discussion of Roulettes although previously, Dürer (1525), D. Bernoulli, la Hire, Desargues, Leibnitz, Newton, Maxwell and others had made contributions in one form or another, particularly on the Cycloidal Curves.

1. GENERAL DISCUSSION: A Roulette is the path of a point - or the envelope of a line - attached to the plane of a curve which rolls upon a fixed curve (with obvious continuity conditions).

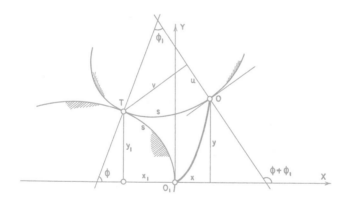

Fig. 159

Consider the Roulette of the point O attached to a curve which rolls upon a fixed curve referred to its tangent and normal at O_1 as axes. Let O be originally at O_1 and let $T:(x_1,y_1)$ be the point of contact. Also let (u,v) be coordinates of T referred to the tangent and normal at O; φ and φ_1 be the angles of the normals as indicated. Then

$$\begin{cases} x = v \cdot \sin(\varphi + \varphi_1) - u \cdot \cos(\varphi + \varphi_1) - x_1 \\ y = -v \cdot \cos(\varphi + \varphi_1) - u \cdot \sin(\varphi + \varphi_1) + y_1 \ , \end{cases}$$

where all the quantities appearing in the right member
may be expressed in terms of OT, the arc length s. These
then are parametric equations of the locus of O. It is
not difficult to generalize for any carried point.

Familiar examples of Roulettes of a point are the
Cycloids, the Trochoids, and Involutes.

2. ROULETTES UPON A LINE:

(a) Polar Equation: Consider the Roulette generated
by the point Q attached to the curve $r = f(\theta)$, referred to Q as pole (with QO_1 as initial line), as it
rolls upon the x-axis. Let P be the point of tangency and the point O_1 of the curve be originally at
O. The instantaneous center of rotation of Q is P and
thus for the locus of Q:

$$\frac{dy}{dx} = \cot \psi$$

But $\tan \psi = r(\frac{d\theta}{dr})$ and

$$y = r \cdot \sin \psi = r(\frac{dx}{ds}).$$

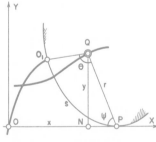

Fig. 160

Thus, among the relations:

$$r = f(\theta), \frac{dx}{dy} = r(\frac{d\theta}{dr}), \ y = r(\frac{dx}{ds})$$

the quantities r, θ may be
eliminated to obtain the
rectangular equation of the
path of Q.

For example, consider, Fig. 161, the locus of the
focus of the Parabola rolling upon a line: originally
the tangent at its vertex:

$$r = \frac{2a}{1 - \sin \theta} \ , \ \ \frac{dx}{dy} = \frac{1 - \sin \theta}{\cos \theta}, \ \ y = r \cdot \frac{dx}{ds} \ .$$

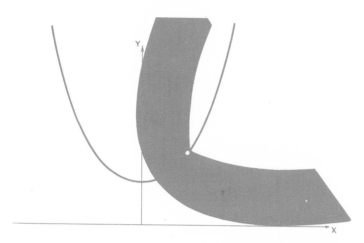

Fig. 161

From these, r and θ are eliminated to give

$$a \cdot ds = y \, dx \text{ or } a \cdot s = \int_o^x y \, dx = A$$

a definitive property of the <u>Catenary</u> (See Catenary, 3).

(b) <u>Pedal</u> <u>Equation</u>: If the rolling curve is in the form $p = f(r)$ (with respect to Q), then $p = QN = y$ $= r(\frac{dx}{ds})$ and the rectangular equation of the roulette is given by:

$$\boxed{y = f(y \cdot \frac{ds}{dx})}$$

For example, consider the Roulette of the pedal point (here the center of the fixed circle) of the <u>Cycloidal</u> <u>family</u>:

$$\boxed{Bp^2 = A^2(r^2 - a^2)}$$ where $A = a + 2b$, and

$B = 4b(a + b)$, as the curve rolls upon the x-axis (originally a cusp tangent).

ROULETTES

The Roulette is given by

$$By^2 = A^2[y^2(\frac{ds}{dx})^2 - a^2] = A^2y^2(1 + y'^2) - a^2A^2.$$

From this

$$\frac{2adx}{A} = \frac{2ydy}{\sqrt{A^2 - y^2}}$$

and

$$\frac{ax}{A} = -\sqrt{A^2 - y^2} \ ,$$

the constant of integration being discarded by choos-
ing the fixed tangent. Thus the Roulette is

$$\boxed{A^2y^2 + a^2x^2 = A^4} \ ,$$

an <u>Ellipse</u>. As a particular case, Fig. 162, the
<u>Cardioid</u> has a = b, and the Roulette of its pedal
point is

$$x^2 + 9y^2 = 81a^2.$$

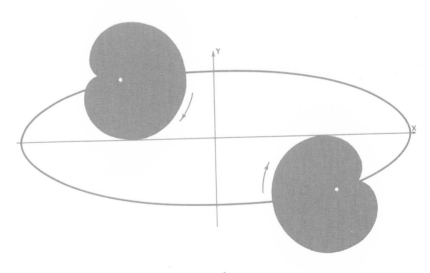

Fig. 162

The Cardioid rolls on "top" of the line until the cusp touches, then upon the "bottom" in the reverse direction.

(c) Elegant theorems due to Steiner connect the areas and lengths of Roulettes and Pedal Curves:

I. Let a point rigidly attached to a closed curve rolling upon a line generate a Roulette through one revolution of the curve. The area between Roulette and line is double the area of the Pedal of the rolling curve with respect to the generating point. For example

> The area under one arch of the Ordinary Cycloid generated by a circle of radius a is $3\pi a^2$; the area of the Cardioid formed as the Pedal of this circle with respect to a point on the circle is $\frac{3\pi a^2}{2}$.

> The Pedal of an Ellipse with respect to a focus is the circle on the major axis (2a) as diameter. Thus the area under the Roulette (an Elliptic Catenary. See 8) of a focus as the Ellipse rolls upon a line is $2\pi a^2$.

II. If any curve roll upon a line, the arc length of the Roulette described by a point is equal to the corresponding arc length of the Pedal with respect to the generating point. For example

> The length, 8a, of one arch of the ordinary Cycloid is the same as that of the Cardioid.

> The length of one arch of the Elliptic Catenary is $2\pi a$, the circumference of the circle on the major axis of the Ellipse.

3. THE LOCUS OF THE CENTER OF CURVATURE OF A CURVE, MEASURED AT THE POINT OF CONTACT, AS THE CURVE ROLLS UPON A LINE:

Let the rolling curve be given by its Whewell

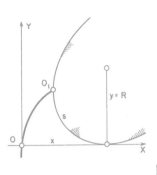

Fig. 163

intrinsic equation: $s = f(\varphi)$. Then, if x,y are coordinates of the center of curvature,

$$x = s = f(\varphi), \quad y = R = f'(\varphi)$$

are parametric equations of the locus. For example, for the Cycloidal family,

$$s = A \cdot \sin B \varphi$$

$$x = A \cdot \sin B\varphi, \quad y = AB \cdot \cos B\varphi$$

and the locus is

$$\boxed{B^2 x^2 + y^2 = A^2 B^2}, \text{ an } \underline{\text{Ellipse}}.$$

4. THE ENVELOPE OF A LINE CARRIED BY A CURVE ROLLING UPON A FIXED LINE:

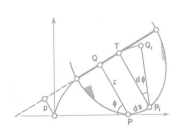

Fig. 164

Draw PQ perpendicular to the carried line. Then Q is the point of tangency of the carried line with its envelope. For, Q has, at the instant pictured, the direction of the carried line and every point of that line has center of rotation at P. The envelope is thus the locus of points Q.

Let the curve roll to a neighboring point P_1 carrying Q to Q_1 through the angle $d\varphi$. Then if σ represents the arc length of the envelope,

$$d\sigma = QT + TQ_1 = \sin\varphi \cdot ds + z \cdot d\varphi,$$

or

$$\frac{d\sigma}{d\varphi} = \sin\varphi \left(\frac{ds}{d\varphi}\right) + z$$

a relation connecting radii of curvature of rolling curve and envelope. Intrinsic equations of the envelope are frequently easily obtained. For example, consider the envelope of a diameter of a circle of radius $\underline{a}$. Here

$$z = a \cdot \sin\varphi$$

and $$\frac{ds}{d\varphi} = a.$$

Thus $$\frac{d\sigma}{d\varphi} = 2a \cdot \sin\varphi \quad \text{and}$$

$$\boxed{\sigma = -2a \cdot \cos\varphi} \quad \text{, an}$$

intrinsic equation of an
ordinary Cycloid.

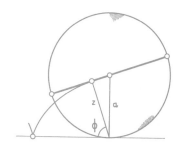

Fig. 165

5. THE ENVELOPE OF A LINE CARRIED BY A CURVE ROLLING UPON A FIXED CURVE:

If one curve rolls upon
another, the envelope of a carried
line is given by

$$\frac{d\sigma}{d\varphi} = z + (\cos\ \alpha) \cdot \frac{R_1 R_2}{(R_1 + R_2)} \ ,$$

where the normals to line and
curves meet at the angle α, and
the R's are radii of curvature of
the curves at their point of
contact.

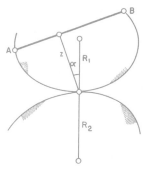

Fig. 166

6. A CURVE ROLLING UPON AN EQUAL CURVE:

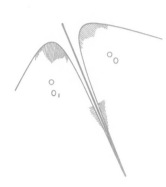

As one curve rolls upon an equal fixed curve with corresponding points in contact, the whole configuration is a reflection in the common tangent (Maclaurin 1720). Thus the Roulette of any carried point O is a curve similar to the pedal with respect to O_1 (the reflection of O) with double its linear dimensions. A simple illustration is the Cardioid. (See Caustics.)

Fig. 167

7. SOME ROULETTES:

Rolling Curve	Fixed Curve	Carried Element	Roulette
Circle	Line	Point of Circle	Cycloid
Parabola	Line	Focus	Catenary (ordinary)*
Ellipse	Line	Focus	Elliptic Catenary*
Hyperbola	Line	Focus	Hyperbolic Catenary*
Reciprocal Spiral	Line	Pole	Tractrix
Involute of Circle	Line	Center of Circle	Parabola
Cycloidal Family	Line	Center	Ellipse
Line	Any Curve	Point of Line	Involute of the Curve
Any Curve	Equal Curve	Any Point	Curve similar to Pedal

SOME ROULETTES (Continued):

Rolling Curve	Fixed Curve	Carried Element	Roulette
Parabola	Equal Parabola	Vertex	Ordinary Cissoid
Circle	Circle	Any Point	Cycloidal Family
Parabola	Line	Directrix	Catenary
Circle	Circle	Any Line	Involute of Epicycloid
Catenary	Line	Any Line	Involute of a Parabola

*The surfaces of revolution of these curves all have constant mean curvature. They appear in minimal problems (soap films).

8. The mechanical arrangement of four bars shown has an action equivalent to Roulettes. The bars, taken equal in pairs, form a <u>crossed</u> <u>parallelogram</u>. If a smaller side AB be fixed to the plane, Fig. 168(a), the longer bars intersect on an Ellipse with A and B as foci. The points C and D are foci of an equal Ellipse tangent to the fixed one at P, and the action is that of rolling Ellipses. (The crossed parallelogram is used as a "quick return" mechanism in machinery.)

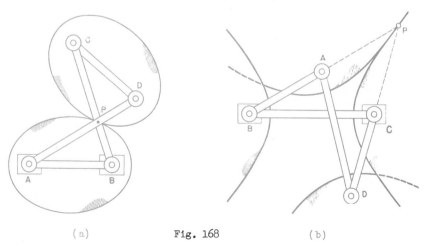

(a)   Fig. 168   (b)

On the other hand, if a long bar BC be fixed to the plane, Fig. 168(b), the short bars (extended) meet on an Hyperbola with B and C as foci. Upon this Hyperbola rolls an equal one with foci A and D, their point of contact at P.

If P (the intersection of the long bars) be moved along a line and toothed wheels placed on the bars BC and AD as shown, Fig. 169(a), the Roulette of C (or D)

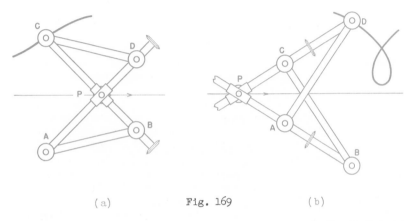

(a)   **Fig. 169**   (b)

is an Elliptic Catenary, a plane section of the <u>Unduloid</u> whose mean curvature is constant. The wheels require the motion of C and D to be at right angles to the bars in order that P be the center of rotation of any point of CD. The action is that of an Ellipse rolling upon the line.

If the intersection of the shorter bars extended, Fig. 169(b), with wheels attached, move along the line, the Roulette of D (or A) is the Hyperbolic Catenary. Here A and D are foci of the Hyperbola which touches the line at P.

BIBLIOGRAPHY

Aoust; Courbes Planes, Paris (1873) 200.
Besant, W. H.: Roulettes and Glissettes, London (1870).
Cohn-Vossen: Anschauliche Geometrie, Berlin (1932) 225.
Encyclopaedia Britannica: "Curves, Special", 14th Ed.
Maxwell, J. C.: Scientific Papers, v 1 (1849).
Moritz, R. E.: U. of Wash. Publ. (1923).
Taylor, C.: Curves Formed by the Action of ... Geometric
    Chucks, London (1874).
Wieleitner, H.: Spezielle ebene Kurven, Leipsig (1908)
    169 ff.
Williamson, B.: Integral Calculus, Longmans, Green (1895)
    203 ff., 238.
Yates, R.C.: Geometrical Tools, Educational Publishers,
    St. Louis (1949).

SEMI-CUBIC PARABOLA

HISTORY: $ay^2 = x^3$ was the first algebraic curve rectified (Neil 1659). Leibnitz in 1687 proposed the problem of finding the curve down which a particle may descend under the force of gravity, falling equal vertical distances in equal time intervals with initial velocity different from zero. Huygens announced the solution as a Semi-Cubic Parabola with a vertical cusp tangent.

DESCRIPTION: The curve is defined by the equation:

$$y^2 = Ax^3 + Bx^2 + Cx + D = A(x - a)(x^2 + bx + c) \ ,$$

which, from a fancied resemblance to botanical items, is sometimes called a Calyx and includes forms known as Tulip, Hyacinth, Convolvulus, Pink, Fucia, Bulbus, etc., according to relative values of the constants. (See Loria.)

In sketching the curve, it will be found convenient to draw as a vertical extension the Cubic Parabola. (See Sketching, 10.)

$$y_1 = y^2 .$$

Values for which y_1 is negative correspond to imaginary values of y. There is symmetry with respect to the x-axis. For example:

$y_1 = y^2 = (x-1)(x-2)(x-3)$ $y_1 = y^2 = (x-1)(x-2)^2$

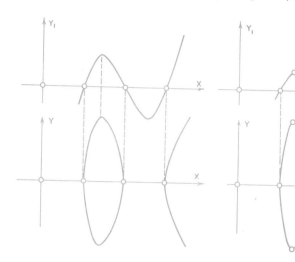

Fig. 170

Slope at $x = 1$ (etc.):   Slope at $x = 2$ (etc.):

$\underset{x \to 1}{\text{Limit}}[\dfrac{y}{(x-1)}] = $

$\underset{x \to 2}{\text{Limit}}[\dfrac{y}{(x-2)}] = $

$\underset{x \to 1}{\text{Limit}}\sqrt{\dfrac{(x-2)(x-3)}{x-1}} = \alpha.$

$\text{Limit} \pm \sqrt{x-1} = \pm 1.$

(NOTE: Scales on X and Y-axes different).

2. GENERAL ITEMS:

(a) The Semi-Cubic Parabola $27ay^2 = 4(x - 2a)^3$ is the Evolute of the Parabola $y^2 = 4ax$.

(b) The Evolute of $ay^2 = x^3$ is

$$a(a - 18x)^3 = [54ax + (\frac{729}{16})y^2 + a^2]^2 .$$

BIBLIOGRAPHY

Loria, G.: Spezielle Algebraische und Transzendte ebene Kurven, Leipsig (1902) 21.

SKETCHING

ALGEBRAIC CURVES: $f(x,y) = 0$.

1. INTERCEPTS - SYMMETRY - EXTENT are items to be noticed at once.

2. ADDITION OF ORDINATES:

The point-wise construction of some functions, $y(x)$, is often facilitated by the addition of component parts. For example (see also Fig. 181):

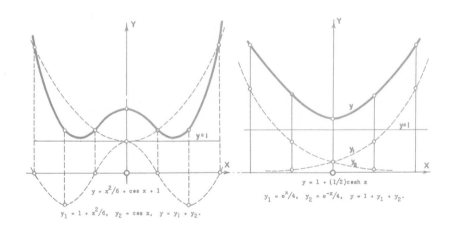

$y = x^2/6 + \cos x + 1$

$y_1 = 1 + x^2/6, \quad y_2 = \cos x, \quad y = y_1 + y_2.$

$y = 1 + (1/2)\cosh x$

$y_1 = e^x/4, \quad y_2 = e^{-x}/4, \quad y = 1 + y_1 + y_2.$

Fig. 171

The general equation of second degree:
$$Ax^2 + 2Bxy + Cy^2 + 2Dx + 2Ey + F = 0 \ldots \ldots (1)$$
may be discussed to advantage in the same manner.

Rewriting (1) as
$$Cy = -Bx - E \pm \sqrt{(B^2 - AC)x^2 + 2(BE - CD)x + E^2 - CF}, \quad C \neq 0,$$
we let $Cy = y_1 \pm y_2$,

where $y_1 = -Bx - E,$ ....(2)

and $y_2 = \sqrt{(B^2 - AC)x^2 + 2(BE - CD)x + E^2 - CF}.$ ..(3)

Here $y_2{}^2 - (B^2 - AC)x^2 - 2(BE - CD)x - E^2 + CF = 0,$

in which it is evident that the conic in (3) or (1) is
an Ellipse if $B^2 - AC < 0,$ an Hyperbola if $B^2 - AC > 0,$
a Parabola if $B^2 - AC = 0.$ The construction is effected
by combining ordinates in (2) and (3):

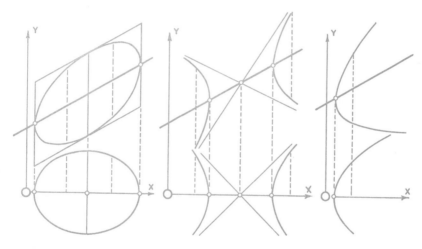

Fig. 172

Some facts are evident:

(a) The center of the conic (1) is at

$$x = \frac{CD - BE}{B^2 - AC}, \qquad\qquad y = \frac{AE - BD}{B^2 - AC}.$$

(b) Since $y_1 = -Bx - E$ bisects all chords $x = k,$ this
line is conjugate to the diameter $x = \dfrac{CD - BE}{B^2 - AC}.$ In
the case of the Parabola, $y_1 = -Bx - E$ is parallel to
the axis of symmetry. This axis of symmetry is thus
inclined at Arc $\tan(\dfrac{-B}{C})$ to the y-axis. The point of
tangency of the tangent with slope $\dfrac{C}{B}$ is the vertex of
the Parabola.

(c) Tangents at the points of intersection of the
line $y_1 = -Bx - E$ and the curve (1) are vertical.
(In connection, see Conics, 4).

3. AUXILIARY AND DIRECTIONAL CURVES: The equations of
some curves may be put into forms where simpler and more
familiar curves appear as helpful guides in certain regions of the plane. For example:

$$y = x^2 - \frac{1}{3x} \qquad\qquad y = e^{-x} \cos x$$

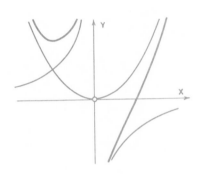 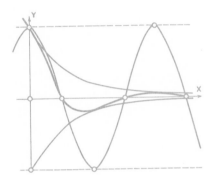

Fig. 173

In the neighborhood of the
origin, $\frac{1}{3x}$ dominates and the
given curve follows the
Hyperbola $y = -\frac{1}{3x}$. As
$x \to \infty$, the term x^2 dominates and the curve follows
the Parabola $y = x^2$.

The quantity e^{-x} here con-
trols the maximum and
minimum values of y and is
called the damping factor.
The curve thus oscillates
between $y = e^{-x}$ and
$y = -e^{-x}$ since $\cos x$ varies
only between -1 and +1.

(See also Fig. 92.)

4. SLOPES AT THE INTERCEPT POINTS AND TANGENTS AT THE
ORIGIN: Let the given curve pass through (a,0). A line
through this point and a neighboring point (x,y) has
slope:

$$\frac{y}{(x-a)} \ . \ \text{Then} \ \underset{x \to a}{\text{Limit}} \frac{y}{(x-a)} = m \ \text{is}$$

the slope of the curve at (a,0).

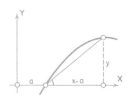

Fig. 174

For example:

$$y = 2x(x - 2)(x - 1)$$

has $m = \underset{x \to 2}{\text{Limit}} \dfrac{y}{(x-2)}$

$$= \underset{x \to 2}{\text{Limit}} \ 2x(x-1) = 4$$

for its slope at (2,0).

$$y^2 = 2x(x - 2)(x - 1)$$

has $m = \underset{x \to 2}{\text{Limit}} \dfrac{y}{(x-2)}$

$$= \underset{x \to 2}{\text{Limit}} \ \pm\sqrt{\frac{2x(x-1)}{(x-2)}}$$

$$= \pm \ \infty$$

for its slope at (2,0).

If a curve passes through the origin, its equation
has no constant term and appears:

$$0 = ax + by + cx^2 + dxy + ey^2 + fx^3 + \dots,$$

or
$$0 = a + b(\tfrac{y}{x}) + cx + dy + ey(\tfrac{y}{x}) + fx^2 + \dots.$$

Taking the limit here as both x and y approach zero, the
quantity $(\tfrac{y}{x})$ approaches $\underline{m}$, the slope of the tangent at
(0,0):

$$0 = a + bm \quad \text{or} \quad m = -\frac{a}{b} \quad \text{whence} \quad \boxed{ax + by = 0} \ .$$

Thus the collection of terms of first degree set equal
to zero, is the equation of the tangent at the origin.

If, however, there are no linear terms, the equation of the curve may be written:

$$0 = c + d\left(\frac{y}{x}\right) + e\left(\frac{y}{x}\right)^2 + fx + \ldots$$

and $0 = c + dm + em^2$

gives the slopes $\underline{m}$ at the origin. The tangents are, setting $m = \frac{y}{x}$:

$$0 = c + d\left(\frac{y}{x}\right) + e\left(\frac{y}{x}\right)^2 \quad \text{or} \quad \boxed{0 = cx^2 + dxy + ey^2} \; .$$

It is now apparent that the collection of terms of lowest degree set equal to zero is the equation of the tangents at the origin. Three cases arise (See Section 7 on Singular Points):

if this equation has no real factors, the curve has no real tangents and the origin is an isolated point of the curve;

if there are distinct linear factors, the curve has distinct tangents and the origin is a node, or multiple point, of the curve;

if there are equal linear factors, the origin is generally a cusp point of the curve. (See Illustrations, 9, for an isolated point where a cusp is indicated.)

For example:

$$y^2 = x^2(x-1) \qquad\qquad y^2 = x^2(1-x) \qquad\qquad y^2 = x^3$$

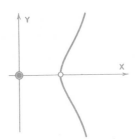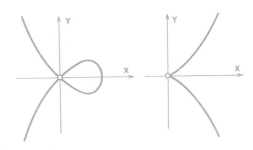

Fig. 175

| has (0,0) as an isolated point | has (0,0) as a node | has (0,0) as a cusp |

5. ASYMPTOTES: For purposes of curve sketching, an asymptote is defined as "a tangent to the curve at infinity". Thus it is asked that the line $y = mx + k$ meet the curve, generally, in two infinite points, obtained in the fashion of a tangent. That is, the simultaneous solution of

$$f(x,y) = 0 \quad \text{and} \quad y = mx + k$$

or $a_n x^n + a_{n-1} x^{n-1} + a_{n-2} x^{n-2} + \ldots + a_1 x + a_0 = 0 \ldots (1)$

where the a's are functions of m and k, must contain two roots $x = \infty$. Now if an equation

$$a_0 z^n + a_1 z^{n-1} + \ldots + a_{n-1} z + a_n = 0 \ldots \ldots (2)$$

has two roots $z = 0$, then $a_n = a_{n-1} = 0$. But if $z = \frac{1}{x}$, this equation reduces to the preceding. Accordingly, an equation such as (1) has two infinite roots if $a_n = a_{n-1} = 0$.

To determine asymptotes, then, set these coefficients equal to zero and solve for simultaneous values of m and k. For example, consider the Folium:

$$x^3 + y^3 - 3xy = 0.$$

If $y = mx + k$:

$(1+m^3)x^3 + 3m(mk-1)x^2$

$+ 3k(mk-1)x + k^3 = 0.$

For an asymptote:

$1 + m^3 = 0 \quad$ or $m = -1$

and $3m(mk-1) = 0 \quad$ or $k = -1$.

Thus $x + y + 1 = 0$ is the asymptote.

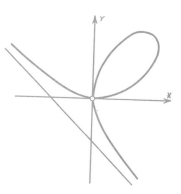

Fig. 176

OBSERVATIONS: Let P_n , Q_n be polynomial functions of x,y of the nth degree, each of which intersects a line in $\underline{n}$ points, real or imaginary. Suppose a given polynomial function can be put into the form:

$$(y - mx - a) \cdot P_{n-1} + Q_{n-1} = 0. \quad \ldots\ldots\ldots\ldots (3)$$

Now <u>any</u> line $y = mx + k$ cuts this curve <u>once</u> at infinity since its simultaneous solution with the curve results in an equation of degree $(n-1)$. This family of parallel lines will thus contain the asymptote. In the case of the Folium just given:

$$(y + x)(x^2 - xy + y^2) - 3xy = 0,$$

the anticipated asymptote has the form: $y + x - k = 0$ and the value of k is readily determined.*

Suppose the given curve of the $\underline{n}$th degree can be written as:

$$(y - mx - k) \cdot P_{n-1} + Q_{n-2} = 0. \quad \ldots\ldots\ldots\ldots (4)$$

Here <u>any</u> line $y - mx - a = 0$ cuts the curve <u>once</u> at infinity; the line $y - mx - k = 0$ in particular cuts <u>twice</u>. Thus, generally, this latter line is an asymptote. For example:

---

*Thus:

$$y = -x + \frac{3xy}{x^2 - xy + y^2} = -x + \frac{3\frac{y}{x}}{1 - \frac{y}{x} + (\frac{y}{x})^2} \cdot$$

As $x,y \to \infty$, $\frac{y}{x} \to -1$ and the last term here $\to \frac{3(-1)}{1 - (-1) + 1} = -1.$

Thus $y = -x - 1$ is the Asymptote.

$$y^3 - x^3 + x = 0 \qquad \Big| \qquad (2y + x)(y - x) - 1 = 0$$

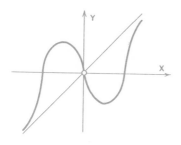 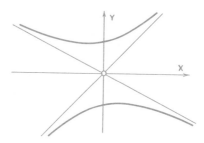

Fig. 177

has $y = x$ for an asymptote. | has asymptotes $2y + x = 0$, $y - x = 0$*

The line $y = mx + k$ meets this curve (4) again in points which lie on $Q_{n-2} = 0$, a curve of degree $(n-2)$. Thus

the three possible asymptotes of a cubic meet the curve again in _three_ finite points upon a line;

the four asymptotes of a quartic meet the curve in _eight_ further points upon a conic; etc.

Thus equations of curves may be fabricated with specified asymptotes which will intersect the curve again in points upon specified curves. For example, a quartic with asymptotes

$$x = 0, \ y = 0, \ y - x = 0, \ y + x = 0$$

meeting the curve again in eight points on the Ellipse $x^2 + 2y^2 = 1$, is:

$$xy\,(x^2 - y^2) - (x^2 + 2y^2 - 1) = 0.$$

---

* In fact, any conic whose equation can be written as $(y-ax)(y-bx)+c=0$ has asymptotes and is accordingly a Hyperbola.

6. CRITICAL POINTS:

(a) <u>Maximum-minimum</u> values <u>of</u> y occur at points (a,b) for which

$$\frac{dy}{dx} = 0, \; \infty$$

with a change in sign of this derivative as x passes through <u>a</u>.

   <u>Maximum-minimum</u> values <u>of</u> x occur at those points (a,b) for which

$$\frac{dx}{dy} = 0, \; \infty$$

with a change in sign of this derivative as y passes through b. For example:

$$y^2 = x^3(1 - x) \qquad\qquad y^3 = (x - 1)^2(x + 1)^9$$

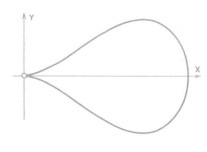 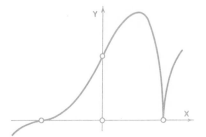

Fig. 178

(b) A <u>Flex</u> occurs at the point (a,b) for which (if y" is continuous)

$$y'' = 0, \; \infty$$

with a change in sign of this derivative as x passes through <u>a</u>. For example, each of the curves:

$$y = x^3, \quad y''_o = 0 \qquad\qquad y^3 = x^5, \quad y''_o = \infty$$

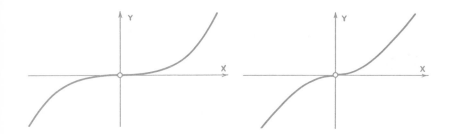

Fig. 179

has a flex point at the origin. Such points mark a change in sign of the curvature (that is, the center of curvature moves from one side of the curve to an opposite side). (See Evolutes.)

<u>Note</u>: Every cubic $y = ax^3 + bx^2 + cx + d$ is symmetrical with respect to its flex.

7. SINGULAR POINTS: The nature of these points, when located at the origin, have already been discussed to some extent under (4). Care must be taken, however, against immature judgment based upon indications only. Properly defined, such points are those which satisfy the conditions:

$$\boxed{f(x,y) = 0, \quad f_x = 0, \quad f_y = 0} \quad,$$

assuming $f(x,y)$ a polynomial, continuous and differentiable. Their character is determined by the quantity:

$$\boxed{F \equiv (f_{xy})^2 - f_{xx} \cdot f_{yy}} \quad.$$

That is, for

      $F < 0$, an <u>isolated</u> (<u>hermit</u>) <u>point</u>,

      $F = 0$, a <u>cusp</u>,

      $F > 0$, a <u>node</u> (double point, triple point, etc.).

Thus, at such a point, the slope: $\frac{dy}{dx} = - (\frac{f_x}{f_y})$ has the indeterminate form $\frac{0}{0}$.

Variations in character are exhibited in the examples which follow (higher singularities, such as a Double Cusp, Osculinflexion, etc., are compounded from these simpler ones).

8. POLYNOMIALS: $\underline{y = P(x)}$ where $P(x)$ is a polynomial (such curves are called "parabolic"). These have the following properties:

(a) continuous for all values of x;

(b) any line $x = k$ cuts the curve in but one point;

(c) extends to infinity in two directions;

(d) there are no asymptotes or singularities;

(e) slope at $(a,0)$ is $\text{Limit}[\frac{P(x)}{x - a}]$ as $x \to a$;

(f) if $(x-a)^k$ is a factor of $P(x)$, the point $(a,0)$ is <u>ordinary</u> if $k = 1$; <u>max-min.</u> if k is even; <u>a flex</u> if k is odd ($\neq 1$).

9. ILLUSTRATIONS:

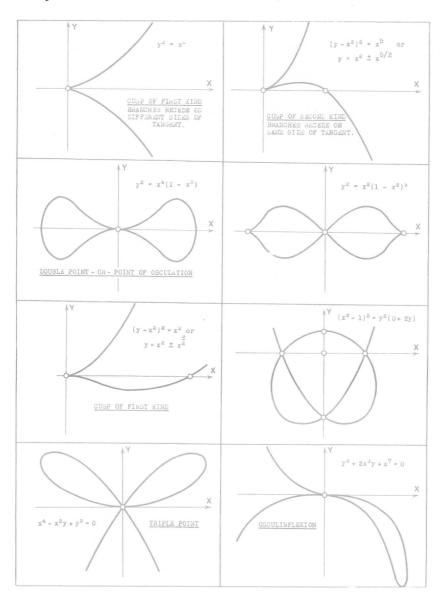

$y^2 = x^3$

CUSP OF FIRST KIND
BRANCHES RECEDE ON
DIFFERENT SIDES OF
TANGENT.

$(y - x^2)^2 = x^5$ or
$y = x^2 \pm x^{5/2}$

CUSP OF SECOND KIND
BRANCHES RECEDE ON
SAME SIDE OF TANGENT.

$y^2 = x^4(1 - x^2)$

DOUBLE POINT - OR - POINT OF OSCULATION

$y^2 = x^2(1 - x^2)^3$

$(y - x^2)^2 = x^3$ or
$y = x^2 \pm x^{\frac{3}{2}}$

CUSP OF FIRST KIND

$(x^2 - 1)^2 = y^2(3 + 2y)$

$x^4 - x^2y + y^3 = 0$ TRIPLE POINT

$y^2 + 2x^3y + x^7 = 0$

OSCULINFLEXION

Fig. 180

ILLUSTRATIONS (Continued):

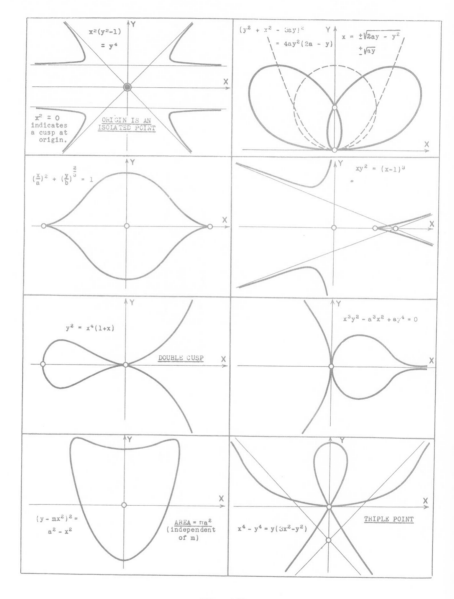

Fig. 181

10. SEMI-POLYNOMINALS: $\underline{y^2 = P(x)}$ where $P(x)$ is a polynomial (such curves are called "semi-parabolic"). In
sketching semi-parabolic
curves, it may be found ex-
pedient to sketch the curve
$Y = P(x)$ and from this obtain the desired curve by
taking the square root of
the ordinates Y. Slopes at
the intercepts should be
checked as indicated in (4).
The example shown is

$$Y = y^2 = x(3 - x)(x - 2)^2.$$

In projecting, the maximum
Y's and y's occur at the
same x's; negative Y's yield
no corresponding y's; the
slope at $(2,0)$ is

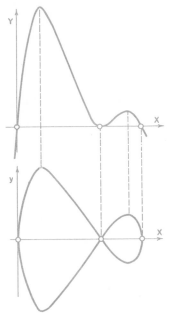

$$\underset{x \to 2}{\text{Limit}} \frac{y}{(x-2)} = \underset{x \to 2}{\text{Limit}} \pm \sqrt{x(3-x)}$$

$$= \pm \sqrt{2}.$$

Fig. 182

11. EXAMPLES:

   (a) <u>Semi-Polynomials</u>

$y^2 = x(x^2 - 1)$	$y^2 = x(1 - x^2)$	$y^2 = x^2(1 - x)$
$y^2 = x^2(x - 1)$	$y^2 = x^2(1 - x^3)$	$y^2 = x^3(1 - x)$
$y^2 = x^3(x - 1)$	$y^2 = x^4(1 - x^3)$	$y^2 = x^4(x^3 - 1)$
$y^2 = x^4(1 - x^2)$	$y^2 = x^4(1 - x^4)$	$y^2 = x^5(x - 1)^4$
$y^2 = (1 - x^2)^3$	$y^2 = x(x - 1)(x - 2)$	$y^2 = x^2(x^2 - 1)(x^2 - 4)^3$

(b) <u>Asymptotes</u>:

$y(a^2 + x^2) = a^2 x$: $[y = 0]$.　　$x^2 y + y^2 x = a^3$: $[x = 0, \; y = 0, \; x + y = 0]$.

$y^3 = x(a^2 - x^2)$: $[x + y = 0]$.　　$x^3 + y^3 = a^3$: $[x + y = 0]$.

$x^3 - a(xy + a^2) = 0$: $[x = 0]$.　　$(2a - x)x^2 - y^3 = 0$: $[x + y = \dfrac{2a}{3}]$.

$y^2(x^2 - y^2) - 2ay^3 + 2a^3 x = 0$: $[y = 0, \; x - y = a, \; x + y + a = 0]$.

$y(y - x)^2(y + 2x) = 9ax^3$.　　$(y - b)(y - c)x^2 = a^2 y^2$.

$x^2 y^2 - a^2 y^2 + b^2 x^2 = 0$.　　$(x - y)\,xy - a(x + y) = b^3$.

$(x-y)^2(x-2y)(x-3y) - 2a(x^3 - y^3) - 2a^2(x+y)(x-2y) = 0$: [four
asymptotes].

$x^2(x+y)(x-y)^2 + ax^3(x-y) - a^2 y^3 = 0$: $[x = \pm a, \; x-y+a = 0, x-y = \dfrac{a}{2}$,

$x+y+\dfrac{a}{2} = 0]$.

$(x^2 - y^2)(y^2 - 4x^2)' - 6x^3 + 5x^2 y + 3xy^2 - 2y^3 - x^2 + 3xy - 1 = 0$

has four asymptotes which cut the curve again in eight points
upon a circle.

$4(x^4 + y^4) - 17x^2 y^2 - 4x(4y^2 - x^2) + 2(x^2 - 2) = 0$ has asymptotes
that cut the curve again in points upon the Ellipse
$x^2 + 4y^2 = 4$.

(c) <u>Singular</u> <u>Points</u>:

$a(y-x)^2 = x^3$ [Cusp].

$(y-2)^2 = x(x-1)^2$ [Double
Point]

$x^4 - 2x^2 y - xy^2 + y^2 = 0$ [Cusp
of second kind at origin]

$y^2 = 2x^2 y + x^4 y - 2x^4$ [Iso-
lated Pt].

$x^3 + 2x^2 + 2xy - y^2 + 5x - 2y$
$= 0$ [Cusp of first kind].

$(2y+x+1)^2 = 4(1-x)^5$ [Cusp].

$a^3 y^2 - 2abx^2 y = x^5$ [Osculin-
flexion].

$y^2 - 2x^2 y + x^4 y + x^4 = 0$ [Double
cusp of second kind at origin].

$y^2 = 2x^2 y + x^4 y + x^4$ [Double
Cusp].

$x^4 - 2ax^2 y - axy^2 + a^2 y^2 = 0$
[Cusp of second kind].

12. SOME CURVES AND THEIR NAMES:

Alysoid (Catenary if a = c): $aR = c^2 + s^2$.

Bowditch Curves (Lissajous): $\begin{cases} x = a \cdot \sin(nt + c) \\ y = b \cdot \sin t \end{cases}$

(See Osgood's Mechanics for figures).

Bullet Nose Curve: $\dfrac{a^2}{x^2} - \dfrac{b^2}{y^2} = 1$.

Cartesian Oval: The locus of points whose distances, r_1, r_2, to two fixed points satisfy the relation: $r_1 + m \cdot r_2 = a$. The central Conics will be recognized as special cases.

Catenary of Uniform Strength: The form of a hanging chain in which linear density is proportional to the tension.

Cochleoid: $r = a \cdot \left(\dfrac{\sin \theta}{\theta}\right)$. This is a projection of a cylindrical Helix.

Cochloid: Another name for the Conchoid of Nicomedes.

Cocked Hat: $(x^2 + 2ay - a^2)^2 = y^2(a^2 - x^2)$.

Cross Curve: $\dfrac{a^2}{x^2} + \dfrac{b^2}{y^2} = 1$.

Devil Curve: $y^4 + ay^2 - x^4 + bx^2 = 0$. This curve is found useful in presenting the theory of Riemann surfaces and Abelian integrals (see AMM, v 34, p 199).

Épi: $r \cdot \cos k\theta = a$ (an inverse of the Roses; a Cotes' Spiral).

Folium: The pedal of a Deltoid with respect to a point on a cusp tangent.

Gerono's Lemniscate: $x^4 = a^2(x^2 - y^2)$.

Hippopede of Eudoxus: The curve of intersection of a circular cylinder and a tangent sphere.

Horopter: The intersection of a cylinder and a Hyperbolic Paraboloid, a curve discovered by Helmholtz in his studies of physical optics.

l'Hospital's Cubic: Identical with the Tschirnhausen Cubic and the Trisectrix of Catalan.

SOME CURVES AND THEIR NAMES (Continued):

Kampyle of Eudoxus: $a^2x^4 = b^4(x^2 + y^2)$: used by Eudoxus to solve the cube root problem.

Kappa Curve: $y^2(x^2 + y^2) = a^2x^2$, or $r = \pm\, a \cdot \cot \theta$.

Lamé Curves: $(\frac{x}{a})^n + (\frac{y}{b})^n = 1$. (See Evolutes).

Pearls of Sluze: $y^n = k(a - x)^p \cdot x^m$, where the exponents are positive integers.

Piriform: $b^2y^2 = x^3(a - x)$. Pear shaped. See this section 6(a).

Poinsot's Spiral: $r \cdot \cosh k\theta = a$.

Quadratrix of Hippias: $r \cdot \sin \theta = \dfrac{2a\theta}{\pi}$.

Rhodoneae (Roses): $r = a \cdot \cos k\theta$. These are Epitrochoids.

Semi-Trident:

$xy^2 = a^3$	: Palm Stems.
$xy^2 = 3b^2(a - x)$	: Archer's Bow.
$x(y^2 + b^2) = aby$	: Twisted Bow.
$x(y^2 - b^2) = aby$	: Pilaster.
$x(y^2 - b^2) = ab^2$	: Tunnel.
$xy^2 = m(x^2 + 2bx + b^2 + c^2)$:	Urn, Goblet.
$b^2xy^2 = (a - x)^3$	: Pyramid.
$c^2xy^2 = (a - x)(b - x)^2$	: Festoon, Hillock, Helmet.
$d^2xy^2 = (x - a)(x - b)(x - c)$	: Flower Pot, Trophy, Swing and Chair, Crane.

Serpentine: A projection of the Horopter.

Spiric Lines of Perseus: Sections of a torus by planes taken parallel to its axis.

Syntractrix: The locus of a point on the tangent to a Tractrix at a constant distance from the point of tangency.

SOME CURVES AND THEIR NAMES (Continued):

Trident: $xy = ax^3 + bx^2 + cx + d$.

Trisectrix of Catalan: Identical with the Tschirn-hausen Cubic, and l'Hospital's Cubic.

Trisectrix of Maclaurin: $x(x^2 + y^2) = a(y^2 - 3x^2)$. A curve resembling the Folium of Descartes which Maclaurin used to trisect the angle.

Tschirnhausen's Cubic: $a = r \cdot \cos^3 \frac{\theta}{3}$, a Sinusoidal Spiral.

Versiera: Identical with the Witch of Agnesi. This is a projection of the Horopter.

Viviani's Curve: The spherical curve $x = a \cdot \sin \varphi \cos \varphi$, $y = a \cdot \cos^2 \varphi$, $z = a \cdot \sin \varphi$, projections of which include the Hyperbola, Lemniscate, Strophoid, and Kappa Curve.

$y^x = x^y$: See A.M.M.: 28 (1921) 141; 38 (1931) 444; Oct. (1933).

BIBLIOGRAPHY

Echols, W. H.: Calculus, Henry Holt (1908) XV.
Frost, P.: Curve Tracing, Macmillan (1892).
Hilton, H.: Plane Algebraic Curves, Oxford (1932).
Loria, G.: Spezielle Algebraische und Transzendente
    ebene Kurven, Leipsig (1902).
Wieleitner, H.: Spezielle ebene Kurven, Leipsig (1908).

SPIRALS

HISTORY: The investigation of Spirals began at least
with the ancient Greeks. The famous Equiangular Spiral
was discovered by Descartes, its properties of self-
reproduction by James (Jacob) Bernoulli (1654-1705) who
requested that the curve be engraved upon his tomb with
the phrase "Eadem mutata resurgo" ("I shall arise the
same, though changed").*

1. EQUIANGULAR SPIRAL: $\boxed{r = a \cdot e^{\theta \cdot \cot \alpha}}$. (Also called
Logarithmic from an equivalent form of its equation.)
Discovered by Descartes in 1638 in a study of dynamics.

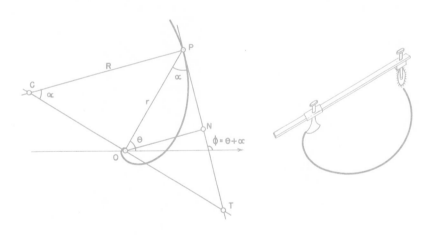

Fig. 183

(a) The curve cuts all radii vectores at a constant
angle α. $(\frac{r}{r'} = \tan \alpha)$.

---

*
Lietzman, W.: Lustiges und Merkwurdiges von Zahlen und Formen,
p. 40, gives a picture of the tombstone.

(b) <u>Curvature</u>: Since $p = r \cdot \sin \alpha$, $R = r \cdot \dfrac{dr}{dp} = r \cdot \csc \alpha = CP$
(the polar normal). $R = s \cdot \cot \alpha$.

(c) <u>Arc Length</u>: $\dfrac{dr}{ds} = (\dfrac{dr}{d\theta})(\dfrac{d\theta}{ds}) = (r \cdot \cot \alpha)(\dfrac{\sin \alpha}{r}) = \cos \alpha$,
and thus $s = r \cdot \sec \alpha = PT$, where <u>s</u> is measured from
the point where $r = 0$. Thus, <u>the arc length is equal
to the polar tangent</u> (Descartes).

(d) Its <u>pedal</u> and thus all successive pedals with
respect to the pole are equal <u>Equiangular Spirals</u>.

(e) <u>Evolute</u>: PC is tangent to the evolute at C and
angle PCO = α. OC is the radius vector of C. Thus the
first and all successive evolutes are equal <u>Equi-
angular Spirals</u>.

(f) Its <u>inverse</u> with respect to the pole is an <u>Equi-
angular Spiral</u>.

(g) It is, Fig. 184, the <u>stereographic projection</u>
$(x = k \tan \dfrac{\varphi}{2} \cos \theta$,

$y = k \tan \dfrac{\varphi}{2} \cdot \sin \theta)$
of a <u>Loxodrome</u>
(the curve cutting
all meridians at a
constant angle: the
course of a ship
holding a fixed
direction on the
compass), from one
of its poles onto
the equator (Hal-
ley 1696).

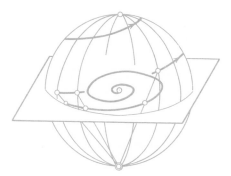

Fig. 184

(h) Its <u>Catacaustic</u> and <u>Diacaustic</u> with the light
source at the pole are <u>Equiangular Spirals</u>.

(i) <u>Lengths of radii</u> drawn at equal angles to each
other form a <u>geometric progression</u>.

(j) <u>Roulette</u>: If the spiral be rolled along a line,
the path of the pole, or of the center of curvature
of the point of contact, is a <u>straight line</u>.

(k) <u>The</u> <u>septa</u> <u>of</u> <u>the</u> <u>Nautilus</u> <u>are</u> <u>Equiangular</u> <u>Spirals</u>. The curve seems also to appear in the arrangement of seeds in the sunflower, the formation of pine cones, and other growths.

Fig. 185

(1) <u>The</u> <u>limit</u> <u>of</u> <u>a</u> <u>succession</u> <u>of</u> <u>Involutes</u> <u>of</u> <u>any</u> <u>given</u> <u>curve</u> <u>is</u> <u>an</u> <u>Equiangular</u> <u>Spiral</u>.

Let the given curve be $\sigma = f(\theta)$ and denote by s_n the arc length of an nth involute. Then all first involutes are given by

$$s_1 = \int_0^\theta (c + f) \, d\theta = c\theta + \int_0^\theta f(\theta) \, d\theta,$$

where <u>c</u> represents the distance measured along the tangent to the given curve. Selecting a particular value for <u>c</u> for all successive involutes:

$$s_2 = \int_0^\theta [c + c\theta + \int_0^\theta f(\theta) \, d\theta] \, d\theta$$

$$.$$
$$.$$
$$.$$

$$s_n = c\theta + c\theta^2/2! + c\theta^3/3! + \ldots + [\int_0^\theta f(\theta) \, d\theta]^{nth},$$

where this <u>nth</u> iterated integral may be shown to approach zero. (See Byerly.) Accordingly,

$$s = \text{Limit}_{n \to \infty} s_n = c\left(\theta + \frac{\theta^2}{2!} + \frac{\theta^3}{3!} + \dots + \frac{\theta^n}{n!} + \dots\right)$$

or
$$\boxed{s = c(e^\theta - 1)} \ ,$$

an <u>Equiangular</u> <u>Spiral</u>.

(m) It is the development of a Conical Helix (See Spiral of Archimedes.)

2. THE SPIRALS: $\boxed{r = a\theta^n}$ include as special cases the

following: $\boxed{n = 1}$: $\boxed{r = a\theta}$ <u>Archimedean</u> (due to

Conan but studied particularly by Archimedes in a tract still extant. He probably used it to square the circle).

(a) Its <u>polar</u> <u>subnormal</u> is constant.

(b) Arc length from 0 to

θ: $s = \frac{a}{2}[\theta\sqrt{1+\theta^2} + \ln(\theta+\sqrt{1+\theta^2})]$

(Archimedes).

(c) $A = \frac{r^3}{6a}$. (from $\theta = 0$
to $\theta = r/a$).

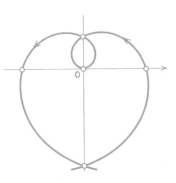

Fig. 186

(d) It is the <u>Pedal</u> of
the <u>Involute</u> <u>of</u> <u>a</u> <u>Circle</u>
with respect to its center. This suggests the description by a <u>carpenter's</u> <u>square</u> rolling without slipping upon a circle, Fig. 187(a). Here OT = AB = a. Let A start at A', B at O. Then AT = arc A'T = r = aθ. Thus B describes the Spiral of Archimedes while A traces an Involute of the Circle. Note that the center of rotation is T. Thus TA and TB, respectively, are normals to the paths of A and B.

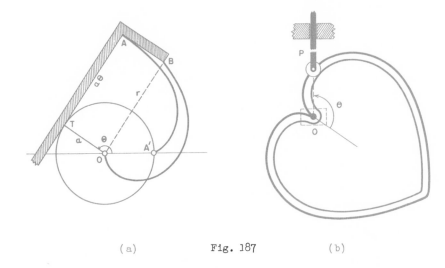

(e) Since $r = a\theta$ and $\dot{r} = a\dot{\theta}$, this spiral has found wide use as a cam, Fig. 187(b) to produce uniform linear motion. The cam is pivoted at the pole and rotated with constant angular velocity. The piston, kept in contact with a spring device, has uniform reciprocating motion.

(f) It is the _Inverse_ of a _Reciprocal_ _Spiral_ with respect to the Pole.

(g) "The _casings_ _of_ _centrifugal_ _pumps_, such as the German supercharger, follow this spiral to allow air which increases uniformly in volume with each degree of rotation of the fan blades to be conducted to the outlet without creating back-pressure." - P. S. Jones, 18th Yearbook, N.C.T.M. (1945) 219.

(h) The ortho-
graphic projection
of a Conical Helix
on a plane per-
pendicular to its
axis is a Spiral
of Archimedes. The
development of
this Helix, how-
ever, is an
Equiangular Spiral
(Fig. 188).

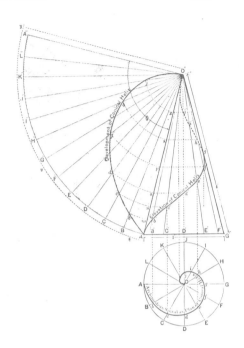

Fig. 188

$\boxed{n = -1}$: $\boxed{r\theta = a}$ Reciprocal (Varignon 1704). (Sometimes called Hyperbolic because of its analogy to the
equation xy = a).

(a) Its polar sub-
tangent is con-
stant.

(b) Its asymptote
is a units from
the initial line.

Limit r·sinθ=
θ → 0

Limit a·$\dfrac{\sin\theta}{\theta}$ = a.
θ → 0

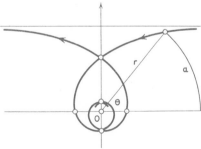

Fig. 189

(c) <u>Arc</u> <u>Lengths</u> of all circles (centers at the pole) measured from the curve to the axis are constant (= a).

(d) The <u>area</u> bounded by the curve and two radii is proportional to the difference of these radii.

(e) It is the <u>inverse</u> with respect to the pole of an Archimedean <u>Spiral</u>.

(f) <u>Roulette</u>: As the curve rolls upon a line, the pole describes a <u>Tractrix</u>.

(g) It is a path of a Particle under a central force which varies as the cube of the distance. (See Lemniscate 4h and Spirals 3f.)

$\boxed{n = 1/2}$: $\boxed{r^2 = a^2\theta}$ <u>Parabolic</u> (because of its analogy to $y^2 = a^2x$) (Fermat 1636).

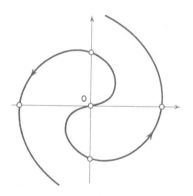

(a) It is the <u>inverse</u> with respect to the pole of a <u>Lituus</u>.

Fig. 190

$\boxed{n = -1/2}$: $\boxed{r^2\theta = a^2}$ <u>Lituus</u> (Cotes, 1722). (Similar in form to an ancient Roman trumpet.)

(a) The <u>areas</u> of all circular sectors OPA are constant $(\frac{r^2\theta}{2} = \frac{a^2}{2})$.

(b) It is the
inverse with re-
spect to the pole
of a Parabolic
Spiral.

(c) Its asymptote
is the initial line.

Limit r·sin θ =
θ → 0

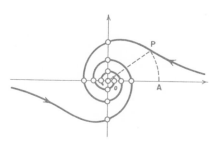

Fig. 191

Limit a√θ sinθ/θ = 0.
θ → 0

(d) The Ionic
Volute: Together
with other spirals,
the Lituus is used
as a volute in
architectural de-
sign. In practice,
the Whorl is made
with the curve

Fig. 192

emanating from a circle drawn about the pole.

3. THE SINUSOIDAL SPIRALS: $r^n = a^n \cos n\theta$ or
$r^n = a^n \sin n\theta$. (n a rational number). Studied by Maclaurin in 1718.

(a) Pedal Equation: $r^{n+1} = a^n p$.

(b) Radius of Curvature: $R = \dfrac{a^n}{(n+1)r^{n-1}} = \dfrac{r^2}{(n+1)p}$
which affords a simple geometrical method of con-
structing the center of curvature.

(c) Its Isoptic is another Sinusoidal Spiral.

(d) It is rectifiable if $\frac{1}{n}$ is an integer.

(e) All <u>positive</u> <u>and</u> <u>negative</u> <u>pedals</u> are again Sinusoidal Spirals.

(f) A body acted upon by a central force inversely proportional to the $(2n + 3)$ power of its distance moves upon a Sinusoidal Spiral.

(g) <u>Special</u> <u>Cases</u>:

n	Curve
-2	Rectangular Hyperbola
-1	Line
-1/2	Parabola
-1/3	Tschirnhausen Cubic
1/3	Cayley's Sextic
1/2	Cardioid
1	Circle
2	Lemniscate

(In connection with this family see also <u>Pedal</u> <u>Equations</u> 6 and <u>Pedal</u> <u>Curves</u> 3).

(h) <u>Tangent</u> <u>Construction</u>: Since $r^{n-1} r' = - a^n \sin n\theta$,

$$\frac{r}{r'} = - \cot n\theta = \cot(\pi - n\theta) = \tan \psi$$

and $\quad \psi = n\theta - \frac{\pi}{2}$

which affords an immediate construction of an arbitrary tangent.

4. EULER'S SPIRAL: (Also called <u>Clothoid</u> or <u>Cornu's</u>
<u>Spiral</u>). Studied by
Euler in 1781 in connec-
tion with an investigation
of an elastic spring.

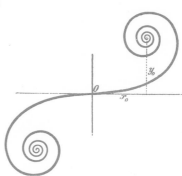

<u>Definition</u>:

$$\left[\begin{array}{l} \sqrt{2t} \cdot dx = a \cdot \sin t \cdot dt \\ \sqrt{2t} \cdot dy = a \cdot \cos t \cdot dt, \end{array}\right.$$

or $\boxed{R \cdot s = a^2}$,

$$s^2 = 2a^2 t$$

<u>Asymptotic</u> <u>Points</u>:

$$x_0, y_0 = \pm \frac{a\sqrt{\pi}}{2}.$$

Fig. 193

(a) It is involved in certain problems in the diffrac-
tion of light.

(b) It has been advocated as a transition curve for
railways. (Since arc length is proportional to curvature. See AMM.)

5. COTES' SPIRALS:
These are the paths
of a particle sub-
ject to a central
force proportional
to the cube of the
distance. The <u>five</u>
varieties are in-
cluded in the equa-
tion:

$$\frac{1}{p^2} = \frac{A}{r^2} + B.$$

They are:

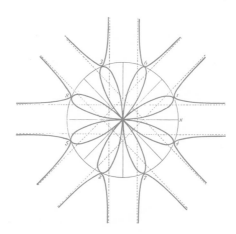

Fig. 194

1. B = 0: the Equiangular Spiral;

2. A = 1: the Reciprocal Spiral;

3. $\dfrac{1}{r}$ = a·sinh nθ;

4. $\dfrac{1}{r}$ = a·cosh nθ;

5. $\dfrac{1}{r}$ = a·sin nθ (the inverse of
                      the Roses).

The figure is that of the Spiral r·sin 4θ = a and its inverse Rose.

The Glissette traced out by the focus of a Parabola sliding between two perpendicular lines is the Cotes' Spiral: r·sin 2θ = a.

BIBLIOGRAPHY

American Mathematical Monthly: v 25, pp. 276-282.
Byerly, W. E.: Calculus, Ginn (1889) 133.
Edwards, J.: Calculus, Macmillan (1892) 329, etc.
Encyclopaedia Britannica: 14th Ed., under "Curves, Special."
Wieleitner, H.: Spezielle ebene Kurven, Leipsig (1908) 247, etc.
Willson, F. N.: Graphics, Graphics Press (1909) 65 ff.

STROPHOID

HISTORY: First conceived by Barrow (Newton's teacher) about 1670.

1. DESCRIPTION: Given the curve $f(x,y) = 0$ and the fixed points O and A. Let K be the intersection with the curve of a variable line through O. The locus of the points P_1 and P_2 on OK such that $KP_1 = KP_2 = KA$ is the general Strophoid.

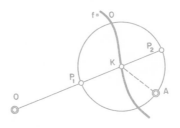

Fig. 195

2. SPECIAL CASES: If the curve $f = 0$ be the line AB and O be taken on the perpendicular OA = a to AB, the curve is the more familiar Right Strophoid shown in Fig. 196(a).

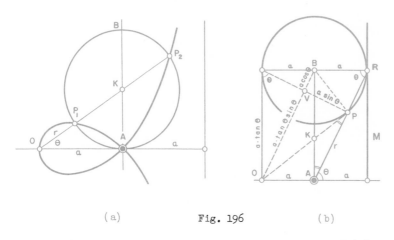

(a)   Fig. 196   (b)

This curve may also be generated as in Fig. 196(b). Here a circle of fixed radius a rolls upon the line M (the

asymptote) touching it at R. The line AR through the
fixed point A, distant <u>a</u> units from M, meets the circle
in P. The locus of P is the Right Strophoid. For,

$$(OV)(VB) = (VP)^2$$

and thus BP is perpendicular to OP. Accordingly, angle
KPA = angle KAP, and so

$$KP = KA,$$

the situation of Fig. 196(a).

The special <u>Oblique</u> <u>Strophoid</u> (Fig. 197(b)) is generated if CA is not perpendicular to AB.

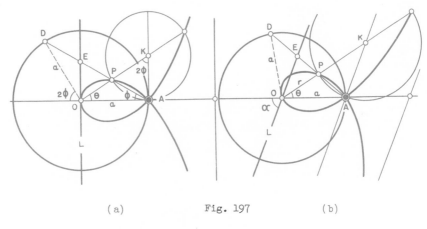

| (a) | Fig. 197 | (b) |

. This Strophoid, formed when f = 0 is a line, can be
identified as a Cissoid of a line and a circle. Thus, in
Fig. 197, draw the fixed circle through A with center at
O. Let E and D be the intersections of AP extended with
the line L and the fixed circle. Then in Fig. 197(a):

$$ED = a \cdot \cos 2\varphi \cdot \sec \varphi$$

and $AP = 2a \cdot \tan \theta \cdot \sin \varphi = 2a \cdot \cot 2\varphi \cdot \sin \varphi.$

Thus $AP = ED,$

and <u>the</u> <u>locus</u> <u>of</u> <u>P, then, is</u> <u>the</u> <u>Cissoid</u> <u>of</u> <u>the</u> <u>line</u> <u>L</u>
<u>and</u> <u>the</u> <u>fixed</u>   <u>circle.</u>

3. EQUATIONS:

Fig. 196(a), 197(a):

$$r = a(\sec\ \theta \pm \tan\ \theta), (\text{Pole at } 0); \text{ or } y^2 = \frac{x(x - a)^2}{2a - x}$$

Fig. 196(b):

$$r = a(\sec\ \theta - 2\cdot\cos\ \theta), (\text{Pole at } A); \text{ or } y^2 = \frac{x^2(a + x)}{a - x}.$$

Fig. 197(b):

$$r = a(\sin\ \alpha - \sin\ \theta)\cdot\csc(\alpha - \theta), (\text{Pole at } 0).$$

4. METRICAL PROPERTIES:

$$A\ (\text{loop, Fig. 196(a)}) = a^2(2 - \frac{\pi}{2}).$$

5. GENERAL ITEMS:

(a) It is the Pedal of a Parabola with respect to any point of its Directrix.

(b) It is the inverse of a Rectangular Hyperbola with respect to a vertex. (See Inversion).

(c) It is a special Kieroid.

(d) It is a sterographic projection of Viviani's Curve.

(e) The Carpenter's Square moves, as in the generation of the Cissoid (see Cissoid 4c), with one edge passing through the fixed point B (Fig. 198) while its corner A moves along the line

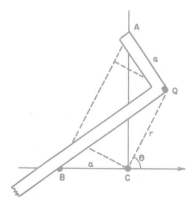

Fig. 198

STROPHOID

AC. If BC = AQ = a and C be taken as the pole of
coordinates, AB = a·sec θ. Thus, the path of Q is the
Strophoid:

$$r = a \cdot \sec\theta - 2a \cdot \cos\theta .$$

BIBLIOGRAPHY

Encyclopaedia Britannica, 14th Ed., under "Curves,
Special."
Niewenglowski, B.: Cours de Géométrie Analytique, Paris
(1895) II, 117.
Wieleitner, H.: Spezielle ebene Kurven, Leipsig (1908).

TRACTRIX

HISTORY: Studied by Huygens in 1692 and later by Leibnitz, Jean Bernoulli, Liouville, and Beltrami. Also called Tractory and Equitangential Curve.

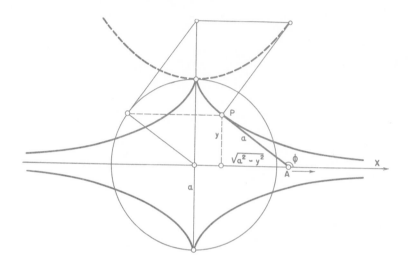

Fig. 199

1. DESCRIPTION: It is the path of a particle P pulled by an inextensible string whose end A moves along a line. The general Tractrix is produced if A moves along any specified curve. This is the track of a toy wagon pulled along by a child; the track of the back wheel of a bicycle.

Let the particle P: (x,y) be pulled with the string AP = $\underline{a}$ by moving A along the x-axis. Then, since the direction of P is always toward A,

$$y' = \frac{y}{\pm \sqrt{a^2 - y^2}}$$.

2. EQUATIONS:

$$x = a \cdot arc\ sech\ \frac{y}{a} - \sqrt{a^2 - y^2}\ .$$

$$\begin{cases} x = a \cdot \ln(\sec\ \theta + \tan\ \theta) - a \cdot \sin\ \theta \\ y = a \cdot \cos\ \theta \end{cases}$$

$$s = a \cdot \ln\ \sec\ \varphi \qquad\qquad a^2 + R^2 = a^2 e^{2s/a}$$

3. METRICAL PROPERTIES:

(a) $K = \dfrac{y'}{a}$ $\qquad\qquad$ $R = a \cdot \cot\ \varphi$

(b) $A = \pi a^2$ $\quad$ [$A = 4 \displaystyle\int_o^a \sqrt{a^2-y^2}\ dy$ (from par. 2, above
$\qquad\qquad\qquad\qquad\qquad\qquad$ = area of the circle
$\qquad\qquad\qquad\qquad\qquad\qquad$ shown)].

(c) $V_x = \dfrac{2\pi a^3}{3}$ (V_x = half the volume of the sphere of
$\qquad\qquad\qquad$ radius a).

(d) $\Sigma_x = 4\pi a^2$ (Σ_x = area of the sphere of radius a).

4. GENERAL ITEMS:

(a) The Tractrix is an involute of the Catenary (see
Fig. 199).

(b) To construct the tangent, draw the circle with
radius a, center at P, cutting the asymptote at A.
The tangent is AP.

(c) Its Radial is a Kappa curve.

(d) Roulette: It is the locus of the pole of a
Reciprocal Spiral rolling upon a straight line.

(e) Schiele's Pivot: The solution of the problem of
the proper form of a pivot revolving in a step where
the wear is to be evenly distributed over the face
of the bearing is an arc of the Tractrix. (See Miller
and Lilly.)

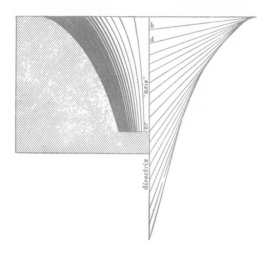

Fig. 200

(f) The Tractrix is utilized in details of mapping. (See Leslie, Craig.)

(g) The _mean_ or _Gauss curvature_ of the surface generated by revolving the curve about its asymptote (the arithmetic mean of maximum and minimum curvature at a point of the surface) is a negative constant ($-1/a$). It is for this reason, together with items (c) and (d) Par. 3, that the surface is called the "pseudo-sphere". It forms a useful model in the study of geometry. (See Wolfe, Eisenhart, Graustein.)

(h) From the primary definition (see figure), it is an orthogonal trajectory of a family of circles of constant radius with centers on a line.

BIBLIOGRAPHY

Craig: Treatise on Projections.
Edwards, J.: Calculus, Macmillan (1892) 357.
Eisenhart, L. P.: Differential Geometry, Ginn (1909).
Encyclopaedia Britannica: 14th Ed. under "Curves,
    Special."
Graustein, W. C.: Differential Geometry, Macmillan
    (1935).
Leslie: Geometrical Analysis (1821).
Miller and Lilly: Mechanics, D. C. Heath (1915) 285.
Salmon, G.: Higher Plane Curves, Dublin (1879) 289.
Wolfe, H. E.: Non Euclidean Geometry, Dryden (1945).

TRIGONOMETRIC FUNCTIONS

HISTORY: Trigonometry seems to have been developed, with certain traces of Indian influence, first by the Arabs about 800 as an aid to the solution of astronomical problems. From them the knowledge probably passed to the Greeks. Johann Müller (c.1464) wrote the first treatise: De triangulis omnimodis; this was followed closely by others.

1. DESCRIPTION:

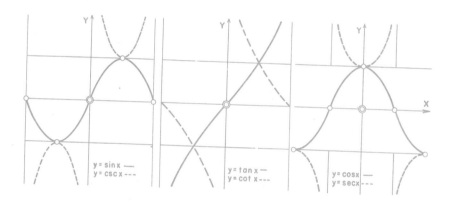

Fig. 201

2. INTERRELATIONS:

(a) From the figure: $(A + B + C = \pi)$

$$\frac{a}{\sin A} = \frac{b}{\sin B} = \frac{c}{\sin C} = 2R \quad ,$$

$$\sin A = \sin(B+C) = \sin B \cos C + \cos B \sin C$$
$$\cos(B+C) = \cos B \cos C - \sin B \sin C$$

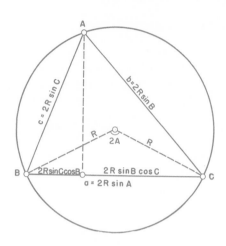

(b) The Euler form:

$$z = e^{ix} = \cos x + i \cdot \sin x;$$

$$\overline{z} = e^{-ix} = \cos x - i \cdot \sin x;$$

$$(\cos x + i \cdot \sin x)^k =$$

$$\cos kx + i \cdot \sin kx$$

produces, on identify-

ing reals and

imaginaries:

Fig. 202

$\sin 2x = 2\sin x \cdot \cos x$	$\cos 2x = 2\cos^2 x - 1$
$\sin 3x = 3\sin x - 4\sin^3 x$	$\cos 3x = 4\cos^3 x - 3\cos x$
$\sin 4x = 4\sin x \cdot \cos x - 8\sin^3 x \cos x$	$\cos 4x = 8\cos^4 x - 8\cos^2 x + 1$

etc.

(c) <u>A</u> Reduction Formula:

$$\cos kx = 2\cos(k-1)x \cdot \cos x - \cos(k-2)x$$
$$\sin kx = 2\sin(k-1)x \cdot \cos x - \sin(k-2)x$$

(d) Since $z^k = \cos kx + i \cdot \sin kx$; $\overline{z}^k = \cos kx - i \cdot \sin kx$,
$z^k + \overline{z}^k = 2 \cdot \cos kx$ and $z^k - \overline{z}^k = 2i \cdot \sin kx$.

Thus to convert from a <u>power</u> of the <u>sine</u> or <u>cosine</u>
into <u>multiple</u> <u>angles</u>, write

$\cos^n x = (\dfrac{z + \overline{z}}{2})^n$, expand and replace $z^k + \overline{z}^k$ by $2 \cdot \cos kx$

$\sin^n x = (\dfrac{z - \overline{z}}{2i})^n$, expand and replace $z^k - \overline{z}^k$ by $2i \cdot \sin kx$,

with $z\overline{z} = 1$.

For example:

$$\sin^2 x = \frac{(1 - \cos 2x)}{2} \qquad \cos^2 x = \frac{(1 + \cos 2x)}{2}$$

$$\sin^3 x = \frac{(3\sin x - \sin 3x)}{4} \qquad \cos^3 x = \frac{(\cos 3x + 3\cos x)}{4}$$

$$\sin^4 x = \frac{(\cos 4x - 4\cos 2x + 3)}{8} \qquad \cos^4 x = \frac{(\cos 4x + 4\cos 2x + 3)}{8}$$

$$\sin^5 x = \frac{(\sin 5x - 5\sin 3x + 10\sin x)}{16}, \qquad \cos^5 x = \frac{(\cos 5x + 5\cos 3x + 10\cos x)}{16}$$

(e)
$$\sum_{k=1}^{n} \sin kx = \frac{\sin \frac{n+1}{2}x \cdot \sin \frac{nx}{2}}{\sin \frac{x}{2}}$$

$$\sum_{k=1}^{n} \cos kx = \frac{\cos \frac{n+1}{2}x \cdot \sin \frac{nx}{2}}{\sin \frac{x}{2}}$$

(f) From the Euler form given in (b):

$$\sin x = -i \cdot \sinh(ix), \qquad \cos x = \cosh(ix)$$
$$\sin(ix) = i \cdot \sinh x, \qquad \cos(ix) = \cosh x$$

3. SERIES:

(a) $\sin x = \sum_{0}^{\infty} (-1)^k \frac{x^{2k+1}}{(2k+1)!}$, $x^2 < \infty$

$\cos x = \sum_{0}^{\infty} (-1)^k \frac{x^{2k}}{(2k)!}$, $x^2 < \infty$

$\tan x = x + \frac{x^3}{3} + \frac{2}{15} x^5 + \frac{17}{315} x^7 + \frac{62}{2835} x^9 + \dots, \; x^2 < \frac{\pi^2}{4}$.

$\cot x = \frac{1}{x} - \frac{x}{3} - \frac{x^3}{45} - \frac{2x^5}{945} - \frac{x^7}{4725} + \dots, \; x^2 < \pi^2,$

$= \frac{1}{x} + \sum_{k=1}^{\infty} \frac{2x}{x^2 - k^2\pi^2}$

$$\sec x = 1 + \frac{x^2}{2} + \frac{5x^4}{24} + \frac{61}{720} x^6 + \frac{277}{8064} x^8 + \ldots, \quad x^2 < \frac{\pi^2}{4}.$$

$$\csc x = \frac{1}{x} + \frac{x}{6} + \frac{7}{360} x^3 + \frac{31}{15120} x^5 + \ldots, \quad x^2 < \pi^2$$

$$= \frac{1}{x} + \sum_{k=1}^{\infty} (-1)^k \frac{2x}{x^2 - k^2\pi^2}.$$

(b) $\quad$ arc $\sin x = x + \frac{1}{2} \cdot \frac{x^3}{3} + \frac{1 \cdot 3}{2 \cdot 4} \cdot \frac{x^5}{5} + \frac{1 \cdot 3 \cdot 5}{2 \cdot 4 \cdot 6} \cdot \frac{x^7}{7} + \ldots, \quad x^2 < 1.$

arc $\cos x = \frac{\pi}{2} - $ arc $\sin x.$

arc $\tan x = x - \frac{x^3}{3} + \frac{x^5}{5} + \ldots, \quad x^2 \leq 1,$

$$= \frac{\pi}{2} - \frac{1}{x} + \frac{1}{3x^3} - \frac{1}{5x^5} + \frac{1}{7x^7} - \ldots, \quad x > 1.$$

arc $\cot x = \frac{\pi}{2} - $ arc $\tan x.$

arc $\sec x = \frac{\pi}{2} - $ arc $\csc x.$

arc $\csc x = \frac{1}{x} + \frac{1}{2} \cdot \frac{1}{3x^3} + \frac{1 \cdot 3}{2 \cdot 4} \cdot \frac{1}{5x^5} + \frac{1 \cdot 3 \cdot 5}{2 \cdot 4 \cdot 6} \cdot \frac{1}{7x^7} + \ldots, \quad x^2 > 1.$

4. DIFFERENTIALS AND INTEGRALS:

$d(\sin x) = \cos x \, dx$ $\qquad\qquad$ $d(\text{arc } \sin x) = \dfrac{dx}{\sqrt{1 - x^2}} = -d(\text{arc } \cos x)$

$d(\cos x) = -\sin x \, dx$

$d(\tan x) = \sec^2 x \, dx$ $\qquad\qquad$ $d(\text{arc } \tan x) = \dfrac{dx}{1 + x^2} = -d'\text{arc } \cot x)$

$d(\cot x) = -\csc^2 x \, dx$

$d(\sec x) = \sec x \tan x \, dx$ $\qquad$ $d(\text{arc } \sec x) = \dfrac{dx}{x\sqrt{x^2 - 1}} = -d(\text{arc } \csc x).$

$d(\csc x) = -\csc x \cot x \, dx.$

$$\int \tan x \, dx = \ln |\sec x|$$

$$\int \cot x \, dx = \ln |\sin x|$$

$$\int \sec x \, dx = \ln |\sec x + \tan x|$$

$$\int \csc x \, dx = \ln |\csc x - \cot x| = \ln \left| \tan \frac{x}{2} \right|.$$

5. GENERAL ITEMS:

(a) <u>Periodicity</u>: All trigonometric functions are periodic. For example:

$y = A \cdot \sin Bx$ has <u>period</u>: $\dfrac{2\pi}{B}$ and <u>amplitude</u>: A.

$y = A \cdot \tan Bx$ has <u>period</u>: $\dfrac{\pi}{B}$.

(b) <u>Harmonic Motion</u> is defined by the differential equation:

$$\boxed{\ddot{s} + B^2 \cdot s = 0}\ .$$

Its solution is $y = A \cdot \cos (Bt + \varphi)$, in which the arbitrary constants are

   A: the <u>amplitude of the vibration</u>,

   φ: the <u>phase-lag</u>.

(c) The Sine (or Cosine) curve is the <u>orthogonal projection</u> of a cylindrical <u>Helix</u>, Fig. 203(a), (a curve cutting all elements of the cylinder at the same angle) onto a plane parallel to the axis of the cylinder (See Cycloid 5e.)

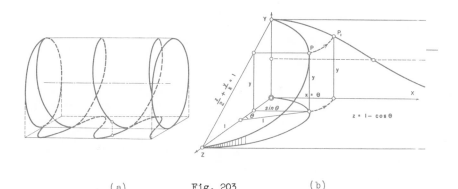

(a)   Fig. 203   (b)

(d) The Sine (or Cosine) curve is the <u>development of an Elliptical section</u> of a right circular cylinder, Fig 203(b). Let the intersecting plane be

$$\frac{z}{2} + \frac{y}{k} = 1$$

and the cylinder: $(z-1)^2 + x^2 = 1$

which rolls upon the XY plane carrying the point
P:(x,y,z) into P$_1$:$(x=\theta,y)$. From the plane:

$$y = k(1 - \frac{z}{2}).$$

But $z = 1 - \cos\theta = 1 - \cos x.$

Thus $\boxed{y = (\frac{k}{2})(1 + \cos x)}$.

A worthwhile model of this may be fashioned from a
roll of paper. When slicing through the roll, do not
flatten it.

(e) <u>A</u> <u>Map</u> <u>of</u> <u>a</u> <u>Great</u> <u>Circle</u> <u>Route</u>:* If an airplane
travels on a great cir-
cle around the earth,
the plane of the great
circle cuts an arbitrary
cylinder circumscribing
the earth in an <u>Ellipse</u>.
If the cylinder be cut
and laid flat as in (d)
above, the 'round-the-
world' course is one
period of a sine curve.
(f) <u>Wave</u> <u>Theory</u>: Trigonometric functions are
fundamental in the de-
velopment of wave theory.
<u>Harmonic</u> <u>analysis</u> seeks
to decompose a resultant
form of vibration into
the simple fundamental
motions characterized by
the Sine or Cosine curve.
This is exhibited in
Fig. 205.

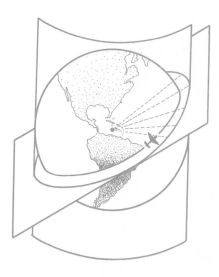

Fig. 204

---

*This is non-conformal (i.e., angles are not preserved).

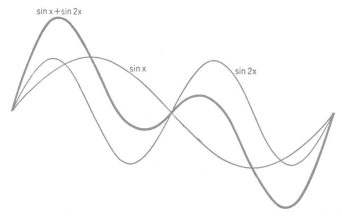

sin x + sin 2x

sin x

sin 2x

Composition of Sounds. A tuning fork with octave overtone would resemble the heavy curve.

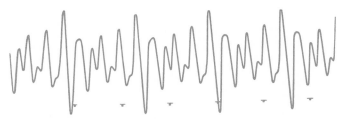

Four Tuning Forks in Unison—Do-Mi-Sol-Do in ratios 4 : 5 : 6 : 8.

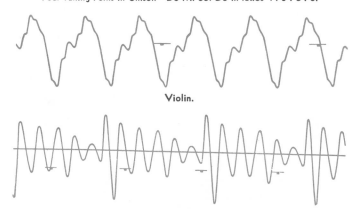

Violin.

French Horn.

Fig. 205

(From Harkin's Fundamental Mathematics. Courtesy of Prentice-Hall.)

Fourier Development of a given function is the composition of fundamental Sine waves of increasing frequency to form successive approximations to the vibration. For example, the "step" function

$$\begin{cases} y = 0, & \text{for } -\pi < x < 0 , \\ y = \pi, & \text{for } 0 < x < \pi , \end{cases}$$

is expressed as

$$y = \frac{\pi}{2} + 2\left(\sin x + \frac{\sin 3x}{3} + \frac{\sin 5x}{5} + \frac{\sin 7x}{7} + \dots\right),$$

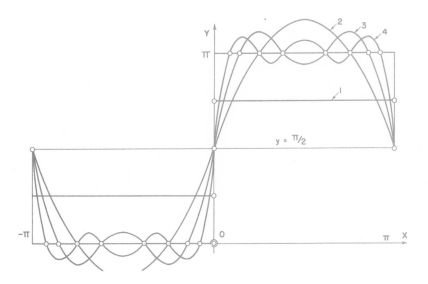

Fig. 206

the first four approximations of which are shown in Fig. 206.

BIBLIOGRAPHY

Byerly, W. E.: Fourier Series, Ginn (1893).
Dwight, H. B.: Tables, Macmillan (1934).

TROCHOIDS

HISTORY: Special Trochoids were first conceived by Dürer in 1525 and by Roemer in 1674, the latter in connection with his study of the best form for gear teeth.

1. DESCRIPTION: Trochoids are <u>Roulettes</u> - the locus of a point rigidly attached to a curve that rolls upon a fixed curve. The name, however, is almost uni- versally applied to Epi- and Hypotrochoids (the path of a point rigidly attached to a circle rolling upon a fixed circle) to which the dis- cussion here is re- stricted.

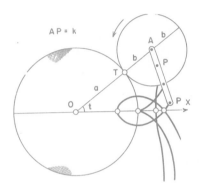

Fig. 207

2. EQUATIONS:

Epitrochoids

$$\begin{cases} x = m \cdot \cos t - k \cdot \cos(mt/b) \\ y = m \cdot \sin t - k \cdot \sin(mt/b) \end{cases}$$

where m = a + b.

Hypotrochoids

$$\begin{cases} x = n \cdot \cos t + k \cdot \cos(nt/b) \\ y = n \cdot \sin t - k \cdot \sin(nt/b) \end{cases}$$

where n = a - b.

(these include the Epi- and Hypocycloids if k = b).

3. GENERAL ITEMS:

(a) The <u>Limacon</u> is the Epitrochoid where a = b.

(b) The <u>Prolate and Curtate Cycloids</u> are Trochoids of a Circle on a line (Fig. 208):

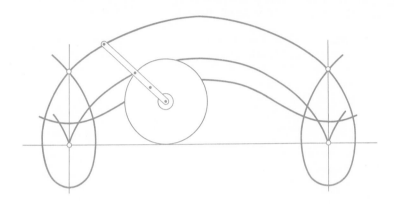

Fig. 208

(c) The <u>Ellipse</u> is the Hypotrochoid where a = 2b. Consider generation by the point P [Fig. 209(a)] . Draw OP to X. Then, since arc TP equals arc TX, P was originally at X and P thus lies always on the line OX. Likewise, the diametrically opposite point Q lies always on OY, the line perpendicular to OX. Every point of the rolling circle accordingly describes a diameter of the fixed circle. The action here then is equivalent to that of a rod sliding with its ends upon two perpendicular lines - that is, a Trammel of Archimedes. <u>Any point F of the rod describes an Ellipse whose axes are OX and OY</u>. Furthermore, any point G, rigidly connected with the rolling circle, describes an Ellipse with the lines traced by the extremities of the diameter through G as axes (Nasir, about 1250).

Note that <u>the diameter PQ envelopes an Astroid with OX and OY as axes. This Astroid is also the envelope of the Ellipses formed by various fixed points F of PQ.</u> (See Envelopes.)

TROCHOIDS 235

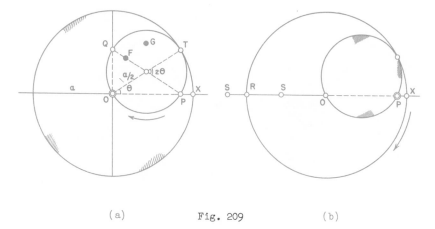

(a)   Fig. 209   (b)

(d) The <u>Double Generation Theorem</u> (see Epicycloids)
applies here. If the smaller circle be fixed [Fig.
209(b)] and the larger one roll upon it, any diameter
RX passes always through a fixed point P on the
smaller circle. Consider any selected point S of this
diameter. Since SO is a constant length and SO extended passes through a fixed point P, the locus of S
is a Limacon (see Limacon for a mechanism based upon
this). Accordingly, <u>any point</u> <u>rigidly</u> <u>attached</u> <u>to</u> <u>the</u>
<u>rolling circle</u> describes a <u>Limacon</u>. If R be taken <u>on</u>
the rolling circle, its path is a <u>Cardioid</u> with cusp
at P.

   <u>Envelope Roulette</u>: Any line rigidly attached to
the rolling circle envelopes a <u>Circle</u>. (See Limacon
3k; Roulettes 4; Glissettes 5.)

(e) The <u>Rose Curves</u>: $r = a \cos n\theta$ and $r = a \sin n\theta$
are <u>Hypotrochoids</u> generated by a circle of radius
$\dfrac{(n-1)a}{2(n+1)}$ rolling within a fixed circle of radius
$\dfrac{na}{(n+1)}$, the generating point of the rolling circle
being $\dfrac{a}{2}$ units distant from its center. (First noticed
by Suardi in 1752 and then by Ridolphi in 1844. See
Loria.)

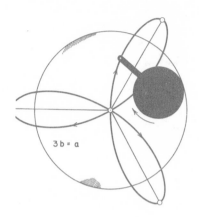

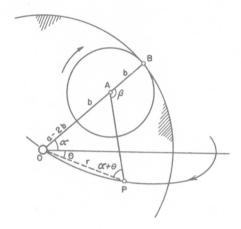

(a)   Fig. 210   (b)

As shown in Fig. 210(b): $OB = a$, $AB = b$, $OA = AP$

$$a\alpha = b\beta, \quad \beta = 2(\alpha + \theta) = \frac{a}{b}\alpha \quad \text{or} \quad \alpha = \frac{2b}{a - 2b}\theta.$$

Thus in polar coordinates with the initial line through the center of the fixed circle and a maximum point of the curve, the path of P is:

$$r = 2(a - b)\cos(\alpha + \theta) = 2(a - b)\cos\frac{a}{a - 2b}\theta.$$

BIBLIOGRAPHY

Atwood and Pengelly: <u>Theoretical</u> <u>Naval</u> <u>Architecture</u> (for connection with study of ocean waves).
Edwards, J.: <u>Calculus</u>, Macmillan (1892) 343 ff.
Loria, G.: <u>Spezielle</u> <u>algebraische</u> <u>und</u> <u>Transzendente</u> <u>ebene</u> <u>Kurven</u>, Leipsig (1902) II 109.
Salmon, G.: <u>Higher</u> <u>Plane</u> <u>Curves</u>, Dublin (1879) VII.
Williamson, B.: <u>Calculus</u>, Longmans, Green (1895) 348 ff.

WITCH OF AGNESI

HISTORY: In 1748, studied and named* by Maria Gaetana
Agnesi (a versatile woman - distinguished as a linguist,
philosopher, and somnambulist), appointed professor of
Mathematics at Bologna by Pope Benedict XIV. Treated
earlier (before 1666) by Fermat and in 1703 by Grandi.
Also called the Versiera.

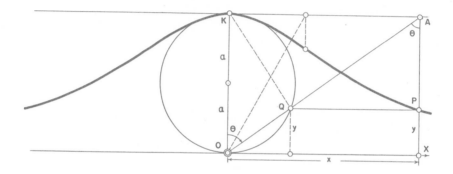

Fig. 211

1. DESCRIPTION: A secant OA through a selected point O
on the fixed circle cuts the circle in Q. QP is drawn
perpendicular to the diameter OK, AP parallel to it.
The path of P is the Witch.

---

* Apparently the result of a misinterpretation. It seems Agnesi con-
fused the old Italian word "versorio" (the name given the curve by
Grandi) which means 'free to move in any direction' with 'versiera'
which means 'goblin', 'bugaboo', 'Devil's wife', etc. [See Scripta
Mathematica, VI (1939) 211; VIII (1941) 135 and School Science and
Mathematics XLVI (1946) 57.]

2. EQUATIONS:

$$\begin{cases} x = 2a \cdot \tan\theta \\ y = 2a \cdot \cos^2\theta \end{cases} \qquad y(x^2 + 4a^2) = 8a^3.$$

3. METRICAL PROPERTIES:

(a) <u>Area</u> between the Witch and its asymptote is four times the area of the given fixed circle ($4\pi a^2$).

(b) <u>Centroid</u> of this area lies at $(0, \frac{a}{2})$.

(c) $V_x = 4\pi^2 a^3$.

(d) Flex points occur at $\theta = \pm\frac{\pi}{6}$.

4. GENERAL ITEMS: A curve called the <u>Pseudo-Witch</u> is produced by doubling the ordinates of the Witch. This curve was studied by J. Gregory in 1658 and used by Leibnitz in 1674 in deriving the famous expression:

$$\frac{\pi}{4} = 1 - \frac{1}{3} + \frac{1}{5} - \frac{1}{7} + \dots .$$

BIBLIOGRAPHY

Edwards, J.: <u>Calculus</u>, Macmillan (1892) 355.
Encyclopaedia <u>Britannica</u>: 14th Ed., under "Curves, Special."

INDEX

(Numbers refer to pages)